EYE IN THE SKY

Introduction to Remote Sensing

Second Edition

Dorothy Harper

Canada Science Series

Published by

Multiscience Publications Limited
Montréal, Québec, Canada, in Association
with Energy, Mines and Resources

ISBN 0-919868-17-7

Catalogue No. M77-5-1983E

FOREWORD TO SECOND EDITION

It is now six years since the first edition of this book appeared. We have seen so much progress in the development of remote sensing techniques during this period that it seemed to be the time to take stock of the situation and to update the earlier edition.

What are the highlights of these new developments?

Probably the most exciting single event in this time was the launching of Seasat in 1978. This satellite, designed mainly for gathering data over the oceans of the world, carried civilian microwave systems into space for the first time. Despite its short life a tremendous amount of data was collected and the excellent detail shown in the imagery exceeded all expectations. There has been a considerable amount of research on microwave methods in general, and some extremely interesting results have been obtained using the synthetic aperture radar system on board the C.C.R.S. Convair-580.

The Landsat series of satellites has continued to operate, and increasing use is being made of some of the weather satellites for studying earth conditions. Great advances have been made in the area of image correction and enhancement techniques, which are allowing us to attain a higher degree of accuracy than we at first thought possible. Digital image correction systems enable the data from different satellites to be brought to a common coordinate system, so that the imagery can be overlaid and directly compared. This will be of great value as more and more satellites of different design, travelling in different orbits, come into operation. The new enhancement methods can be applied to old records now stored on computer-compatible tapes. A permanent file of tapes now exists going back to the first flights of Landsat-I and the tremendous amount of data we now have stored about the earth boggles the mind.

In the air, where experimental methods of making measurements can more easily be carried out, there have been noteworthy advances in infrared scanning systems, high precision spectrometry with much better spectral resolution, laser techniques and microwave systems. These in turn will aid in the design of space systems of the future.

One of the interesting facets of this work has been to see methods, which not long ago were regarded by the layman as being "ivory tower" ideas, now being put to very practical use. Research methods have become operational. We see this particularly in the areas of agriculture and forestry. Change detection methods have allowed changes in the environment to be monitored on a regular basis, and again we can go back to past records and compare conditions then and now. Whereas a few years ago most of the research and development was carried out in government departments and universities, to-day a great deal of it has moved out into the industrial sphere. Industry has accepted the challenges of adapting old methods and creating new equipment. We might almost say that a new industry has been born with all the sociological benefits that this implies. New jobs have been created for Canadians, and Canadian technology has been advanced.

One of the interesting sidelights of this expansion has been the spin-off benefits, so to speak, of using the technology developed for the space age again in other totally unrelated fields. Developments in image analysis, for example, are finding application in medicine - for brain scanning, detection of tumours, improvement of X-ray pictures, etc.. Remote sensing techniques are being applied to the design of robots, which can replace humans in dangerous situations.

The book is well illustrated with black and white and coloured imagery. It is unfortunate, however, that reproductions are never as good as the originals, especially when the pictures are reduced in size. For those interested originals may be ordered from the Canada Centre for Remote Sensing at the address given on p.123.

The update of this book has given me a great deal of personal pleasure. It has allowed me to maintain my faith in the excellence of Canadian scientists and Canadian institutions and has allowed me to renew friendships with scientists working on remote sensing in many parts of Canada. I owe them a debt of gratitude; there have been too many to list individually, but each has given generously of his time and knowledge, and many have checked parts of my manuscript and made valuable suggestions. I must stress however that the responsibility for the manuscript is mine, and the blame for any errors must be laid at my door.

The collection of data, the writing and the travelling associated with a project of this sort is an expensive proposition; it would not have been possible for me without the generous support of the Canada Centre for Remote Sensing who contributed to the cost of writing and travelling. I wish to express my appreciation for their financial contributions.

In conclusion I also wish to express my thanks to Darlene Li, who has typed the whole of this manuscript, in parts many times over. She has always been efficient and cheerful in the face of typing, re-typing and re-re-typing. I hope she will be at hand when I do my next edition.

Dorothy Harper
Victoria, B.C.

January, 1983

PREFACE

(to first edition)

The dominant aspect of the technology of remote sensing to those who are engaged in its full-time pursuit is the rapidity of change. One hardly has time to digest and use new instruments and methods before even newer ones impinge on all sides. Dorothy Harper, I feel, has delightfully captured the flavour of this exciting new technology in a certain time and space. The time is 1969-76 and the space is Canada. In her writing the author has managed to strike the happy compromise between over-simplification and complexity – a rare gift which is sorely needed in this age to explain technology to the layman.

Canada first became involved in 1969 when we formally requested NASA to be permitted to read out her Earth Resources Technology Satellite (ERTS) from Prince Albert, Saskatchewan, and the rest of the Canadian National Program was then built around ERTS (later called Landsat).

I think it is appropriate that such a book should be written by a physicist and spectroscopist because spectroscopy forms the physical basis of remote sensing; I have always maintained that spectroscopists and astronomers were really the first genuine remote sensors.

We are now in the process of planning for the Post-ERTS era which is doubly complex because it involves political aspects as well as state-of-the-art techniques in electronic and space research.

L. W. Morley
Director-General
Canada Centre for Remote Sensing
Ottawa

March, 1976

FOREWORD

(to first edition)

One of the most exciting developments of modern times has been the advent of satellites - satellites for weather forecasting, for communications, for studying the earth and for investigating the heavens and other planets. I have chosen to deal with just one of these aspects - the study of our earth and our environment by the Earth Resource Technology Satellite, which was put into orbit by the U.S. National Aeronautics and Space Administration (NASA) in July, 1972. This was originally called ERTS-1, but when a second similar satellite was launched on January 22, 1975, the two satellites were re-named Landsat-1 and -11 respectively. Throughout the text I have referred to these satellites under the name of Landsat, since we must look to the future rather than to the past. Articles and references published in the past, however, cannot be changed; to avoid confusion we must remember that ERTS and Landsat are the same satellite.

It is the United States whom we must thank for putting these satellites in the sky above us and for allowing us to gather information about our own land; Canada has played an important role in developing means of receiving, enhancing and interpreting the data transmitted earthward. The extent of this data and the information we have derived from it is wonderful indeed and is proving of inestimable value in studying natural resources (forests, terrain, water and ice, crops, geothermal sources, and other environmental conditions). Space methods are of special interest to us in Canada, where the land is very extensive and many areas are inaccessible. To those who question the cost of space research we must reply that the rewards are commensurate with the cost, and have, in fact, turned out to be even greater than had originally been expected. Before Landsat-1 was launched, an estimate was made of the financial benefits to be gained by joining the NASA programme. Actual benefits have outstripped even the most optimistic estimates. The satellite itself has sent us more informative data than we dared hope for and the application of this to practical problems has proved more advantageous than we had expected. This is particularly true in Arctic areas where valid information was woefully lacking at a time when unprecedented expansion was taking place.

Space instruments are allowing us to look at the earth with new eyes; they have extended the scope of our vision. However, they are only one in our compendium of tools for looking at the earth from above. Instruments may also be carried aloft by aircraft, helicopters, balloons and rockets and each of these operating at a different height will tell us something different. The history of surveying from aircraft is an old and honorable one, and aircraft are by no means out-dated by the newer use of satellites. The development of new photographic techniques and other forms of imagery have kept aerial methods to the fore, and the experience gained with aircraft has contributed to the spectacular success obtained with satellites. Some of these methods have been outlined in this book. If the space allotted them is not in accordance with their achievements or importance, it is because so much has already been better written by others, and several relevant books are listed at the end of this one.

The wealth of new knowledge we are gaining about our resources by remote-sensing methods should be invaluable to the developing countries; it is good to know that this information is being shared and is being made available to them in a variety of ways. Some of them are considering erecting their own ground receiving stations, some have been assisted by projects initiated by the Food and Agricultural Organisation and others are receiving information from NASA. There is an awareness among the wealthier nations of the moral responsibility of making this new knowledge available to all and a great deal of thought and planning is going into making this dream a reality.

It is usual in a book of this kind to list in the foreword all those who have helped in its creation. I find the task too difficult. There were too many and the selection of a few names would be an invidious task. In gathering the information I have visited nearly a hundred scientists in various institutions across Canada. Without exception they have been generous of their time and knowledge. They have provided me with notes, photographs, diagrams and inspiration. My thanks to them are boundless and sincere. I must however make special mention of the members of the staff of the Canada Centre for Remote Sensing at Ottawa who have been especially helpful and have put up with my pestering over the past eighteen months with unfailing good humour. Many of them have checked parts of my manuscript and have made valuable suggestions.

In conclusion I must say a special thank you to two people who, though not connected in any way with remote sensing, have carefully read and checked the whole of my manuscript. Professor Harry Dutton, chairman of the Physics Department of Bishop's University, has read it and his critical faculty has been a very great help to me. My sister, Dr. Kathleen Harper, also of Bishop's University and a Professor of English, has checked my spelling, punctuation and atrocious grammar! If at times the expression leaves something to be desired by the purist, it is because I have been anxious to avoid the pedantic and have rather leaned towards the colloquial. (As an example, I prefer to use the word "data" as a singular noun where it refers to a collection of facts, despite its Latin plural form.)

I have enjoyed writing this book. It has been a most rewarding experience, and it now remains for me to say that I hope you will enjoy reading it. It has been written for the non-specialist, for the educated layman, and for the scientifically inclined high school or junior college student. I would hope that some members of the University community, particularly in the disciplines of geography, agriculture and forestry, will also find something to interest them. It is a fascinating field for students to enter and one with a great future.

Dorothy Harper
Bishop's University
Lennoxville, P.Q.
Canada

March, 1976

CONTENTS

CHAPTER I

BEGINNINGS — WHAT IT'S ALL ABOUT

Amid swirling, flaming gases 184 lbs of steel was lifted off the ground for its journey into space. The date was October 4, 1957. Named Sputnik, it was the first artificial satellite to be put into orbit round the earth, and the honour of this accomplishment must go to the U.S.S.R. Most of us who heard the news on the radio the next day experienced a feeling of awe and also a certain degree of apprehension. A new door into the unknown had been opened. What lay on the other side? Would this new development be used for hostile purposes? Or would it be used for the good of mankind rather than for its destruction? Many questions arose in men's minds, and the very newness of the situation made these questions difficult to answer.

Now, nearly twenty-five years later, we have seen the launching of many thousands of such satellites, which have been put into orbit round the earth, the sun, the moon and other planets; we have seen manned space flights, and also spacecraft which will travel prodigious distances through the Universe never to return. The instruments which they carry are sending back to earth a vast amount of information of a new kind which it would be impossible for us to get in any other way. In particular, they are extending the scope of our vision, and the prospects are truly exciting.

These new developments are part of a branch of science known as remote sensing.

Remote sensing, as the words imply, means sensing things at a distance; that is, detecting and measuring some property of an object without actually coming into contact with it. An astronaut going to the moon feels its surface to be dry and powdery. This is not remote sensing; he is there; he can feel it. But you sitting at home in a comfortable chair in front of your T.V. set may watch a cloud of dust arise as his landing gear strikes the moon's surface and so deduce that this is so. This is remote sensing. You are not there (except in imagination); you cannot feel it. Galileo was an early remote senser when he looked at the heavens through his telescope. The pilot of a helicopter is a remote senser as he watches the patterns of traffic on the roads below him and reports back to earth on traffic jams in the morning rush hour. We act as remote sensers when we bask in the sun and feel its warmth, when we watch a horse race or listen to the water boil in a kettle. Our senses of touch, sight and hearing are not in contact with any of these objects; they are working at a distance. From our sense of warmth we can deduce that the sun is hot; from our sense of sight we can deduce the speed of a horse; from our sense of hearing we can deduce that the temperature of the water in the kettle has reached boiling point.

These are really all examples of remote sensing; however, in the world of science this term has come to have a more restricted meaning, and for the purpose of this book we are going to consider only the sensing and measurement of our earth's resources and environment as may be carried out by instruments above the earth. Many of these instruments are basically cameras of one sort or another — ordinary cameras with black and white or colour film, infrared and ultraviolet cameras, T.V. cameras, and so on. They may be carried aloft by rockets and balloons, planes and helicopters, and now by satellites.

Some of the first experiments on photography from the air were made by a French photographer, Felix Tournachon, who took aerial photographs of Paris from a balloon. This was in 1856. Methods and instruments have been steadily improving since that time until to-day we have highly sophisticated instruments which can be carried by satellites, continuously travelling round the earth in predetermined orbits. This is what has dramatically given a whole new dimension to the science of remote sensing.

What good is all this? What is it going to do for you and me?

Some of the most practical early results were obtained by Landsat I launched in the U.S. in July, 1972, by the National Aeronautics and Space Administration (NASA). It was originally called ERTS (Earth Resource Technology Satellite) but its name was changed to Landsat I when a second similar satellite Landsat II was launched in February, 1975. Although it was the U.S. who put these satellites in the sky nearly 600 miles above us, all other countries may by arrangement with NASA take advantage of the data that they send back. And what a wealth of information they provide! In fact, it is almost too much; we have an embarrassment of riches. For example, in Canada alone Landsat is sending back about 75,000 records of the earth's surface every year. The handling of the data and the interpretation of it is a Herculean task, requiring special ground receiving stations, and highly specialized personnel. Communication of the information to those concerned is a headache in itself. Some of it, such as the information on forest fires, the travel of ice across shipping lanes, the effects of flooding in the spring and other emergencies would be useless unless it could be transmitted to those in charge quickly enough to enable them to remedy the situation. Other data, such as the plotting of inland lakes and other terrain characteristics, do not need to be handled quite so quickly. One direct result of this information is that we find some of our maps, particularly in remote places like the Arctic, will have to be redrawn. Some of the islands shown in our geography books, for example, are just not there.

It is easy to see that remote sensing is a particularly valuable tool to countries like Canada and Australia which have large tracts of land, much of which is inaccessible. Data may be gathered over large areas at a fraction of the cost and in a fraction of the time that would be required by more conventional means. We have already had personal experience of the method from weather forecasting pictures on our T.V. sets.

Remote sensing is able to tell foresters a great deal about their forests — the type and extent of the trees, the damage being done to them by disease, by logging, or by environmental changes. It is able to help the geologist by telling him something about the mineralogical condition of the soils, which may point to possible ore deposits or to areas which are worthy of further exploration. It provides a new mapping technique for the geographer, a means of forecasting crop yields for the agriculturist, and a way of monitoring and identifying oil slicks and other pollutants for the environmentalist.

For Canada the most valuable information provided has probably been that in connection with the Arctic and northern areas. These are regions about which we know only too little. With the increase of activity in mineral and oil exploration it is essential that our knowledge of climate, ice formation, terrain and other environmental features should be augmented. Not only do we want to know the effect of the environment on man, but also the effect of man on the environment, and, of course, we can assess this only if we know what the conditions were before large scale human activity took place. Landsat has come along in the nick of time. The whole satellite programme has proved of inestimable value to shipping crews, construction engineers, geologists and others, and has resulted in the saving of many millions of dollars.

Since, in an orbiting satellite, instruments are carried over the same spot on earth at regular intervals of time and at the same time of day (in the case of Landsat every 18 days), it means that slow changes can be observed — for example, the movement of ice floes across shipping lanes, the rate of break-up of ice in the lakes and rivers, and the changing pattern of coast lines brought about by erosion and drifting sands.

All of these things can now be done on a global scale, an accomplishment never before possible. The information will be of great value to the developing countries, enabling them to assess their resources quickly and economically. Some of these may have receiving stations of their own; means are being investigated for conveying the data to others with the utmost speed. The satellites are up there; they are sending back a prodigious amount of information; we must use it wisely and effectively.

You can see, therefore, that satellite and space research is not merely "pie-in-the-sky" for a few wealthy nations that do not seem to know what to do with their money. It is an "eye-in-the sky" for all people and is yielding very practical and down-to-earth benefits for all of us. Its potential is enormous.

As we said before, remote sensing is teaching us a new way of seeing. Before going into how this comes about we should consider how, in fact, we do see things, and how it is that we see different things in different colours.

We see most of the objects about us by reflected light — light from the sun by day, and light from artificial sources by night. Turn off the light and we no longer see anything; there are no light rays for the objects to reflect. These reflected rays of light then pass through the lens of the eye and are focused on the retina; here they stimulate certain cells which send a message to the brain. An eye is very like a camera. Each has a lens; in the case of the camera the scene is focused on the film; in the case of the eye it is focused on the retina.

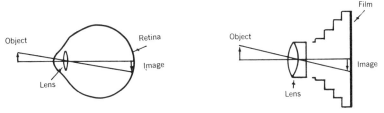

Figure 1. Diagram of the Human Eye and a Camera.

So, this is all brought about by light. What is light? Everybody knows what light is, and ironically this makes it difficult to explain. Light is a form of electromagnetic radiation like radio waves and x rays. They all travel as a wave motion in a straight line. The distance from one wave to the next, say from the peak of one wave to the peak of the next, is called the wavelength, and is generally denoted by the Greek letter, lambda (λ). The different properties and characteristics of these waves are dictated by their wavelengths, so that one wavelength will show the properties characteristic of radio waves, another the properties characteristic of light waves and so on.

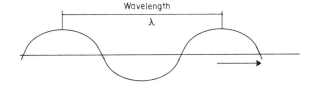

Figure 2. Outline of a Characteristic Wave.

In order to envisage these waves a little better, let us turn our thoughts to a more tangible form of wave motion — that in water, for example. A stone dropped into a pond will start a system of waves which will travel across the pond at a definite speed. As we do not need to deal with actual figures, we will just call this speed **s**. Again the distance from one crest to the next we will call the wavelength λ . If we imagine a post fixed upright in the pond we can count the number of waves passing this point in a certain interval of time, say a minute. This will give us the frequency of the waves, perhaps about 30 per minute. This we will call **f**. Now it is easy to see that if the wavelength is long (i.e. λ is large) the frequency will be small. Provided the speed remains constant, as the distance between the crests becomes smaller (i.e. the wavelength is reduced), the frequency, f, with which they pass this post will become greater. Expressed more exactly as a formula we can say that

$$f \;=\; \frac{s}{\lambda}$$

or alternatively

$$\lambda \;=\; \frac{s}{f}$$

Light is a wave motion which travels through the air at very high speeds indeed; in fact, all electromagnetic radiation travels at this high speed, namely, about 186,000 miles per second, or 300,000,000 metres per second. We will call this c, since it is a constant, and so for electromagnetic radiation we can say that

$$\lambda \;=\; \frac{c}{f} \;,\; \text{or } f \;=\; \frac{c}{\lambda}$$

Whether we choose to describe a wave in terms of its wavelength or in terms of its frequency makes no difference, although it is customary to identify the short waves, such as x rays, visible light and infrared, and sometimes microwaves by their wavelength, whereas the longer waves in the radio part of the spectrum are generally identified by their frequency.

The fact that radiation is propagated in the form of a wave leads to some interesting results; in fact, practically the whole science of optics and spectroscopy is involved with this aspect of light. Of particular relevance to remote sensing are the phenomena of coherence, polarization, Doppler effect, and colour.

As we see, a wave can be characterized by its wavelength. Another characteristic is the amplitude, or the height of the wave. In figure 3 we have two waves (a) and (b), where (b) is twice as high as (a). The amplitude tells us something about the intensity of the radiation — the greater the amplitude the more intense is the radiation — but (and this is extremely important) a wave twice as high produces an intensity not only twice as great but four times as great. If we look at wave (c), which has twice the amplitude of (b), it will produce an intensity four times as great as that of (b) or sixteen times as great as that of (a). In other words the intensity of a light source varies as the square of the amplitude of the wave it produces. If you double the amplitude you increase the intensity by a factor of four; if you treble the amplitude you increase the intensity by a factor of nine, and so on.

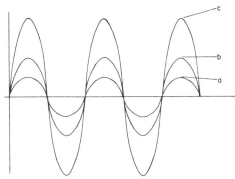

Figure 3. Three Waves with Different Amplitudes.

Now if 2 waves are sent out in exactly the same direction and of exactly the same wavelength (i.e. they are said to be monochromatic), their amplitudes may be added together. Whether this will result in more light or less light will depend on the relative phase of the waves, i.e. whether or not they are in step so that their peaks and valleys coincide. Figure 4(a) shows two waves in phase (coherence), while (b) shows two waves completely out of phase (incoherence), and the dotted line in each case shows the result of adding them together. In (a) the two superimposed waves are shown slightly displaced and in (b) the resultant is shown slightly displaced above the axis; this is merely to make them both visible; they should really lie on top of each other.

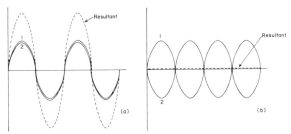

Figure 4.   Coherence (a) and Incoherence (b).

The result is that, if we have two waves of the same wavelength and the same amplitude superimposed in phase, their amplitude will be doubled and the intensity will be quadrupled. If they are completely out of phase, they will cancel each other out and there will be no light at all. If 10 such waves were superimposed in phase the intensity would be increased a hundredfold. It is on this principle that the operation of the laser depends.

Although we have illustrated the characteristics of amplitude, phase and coherence by talking about light waves, the same arguments apply to any other kind of electromagnetic wave, such as microwaves which we cannot see.

Another interesting phenomenon associated with wave motion is polarization. We will see later that it has particular application to the reflection of microwaves.

So far we have been considering wave motion as though it were taking place in one plane only, the plane of the paper, rather like a snake wriggling forward along the ground. A snake progresses with horizontal oscillations to and fro. A caterpillar, on the other hand, progresses by arching its body up and down; it is performing vertical oscillations. We might say the snake's motion is horizontally polarized, while the caterpillar's motion is vertically polarized. So with electromagnetic waves which are travelling in three-dimensional space. They may oscillate up and down (vertical polarization) or they may oscillate to and fro parallel to the ground (horizontal polarization), or they may oscillate in any other plane. With an ordinary light source each train of waves will oscillate in a random manner, some in one direction and some in another, and the light will be unpolarized. We have been looking at a diagram of a wave from the side at right angles to the direction of propagation. Suppose now we look at a bundle of rays head on as they travel towards us; we can then represent the oscillations as in Figure 5.

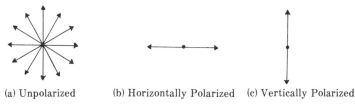

(a) Unpolarized   (b) Horizontally Polarized   (c) Vertically Polarized

Figure 5.   Polarization of Light.

Although light as we see it from usual light sources is unpolarized, various methods are available for tidying up, so to speak, this rather random state of affairs and persuading the waves to oscillate in the same plane. For most purposes it does not matter what state of polarization they are in. Lasers are frequently designed to produce a polarized beam. Microwaves transmitted from linear aerials are also polarized. Some substances are capable of rotating the plane of polarization of a light beam passing through them. Other materials and structures may modify the state of polarization of a light beam reflected from their surface and, as we shall see later, this fact is made use of in the application of radar and other microwave techniques.

Another wave phenomenon of importance in the microwave region is the Doppler Effect. In discussing wavelength and wave propagation we have assumed that the source is stationary. But now let us imagine the source to be moving; this will affect the wavelength of the ray as it reaches us. Suppose again we look at a light source which is moving towards us. The waves in front of this moving source will be squashed together, so to speak, while those behind it will be opened out. Therefore in front the wavelength will appear shorter or the frequency will appear greater, while behind the wavelength will appear longer or the frequency will appear lower. The extent to which the wavelength is changed is called the Doppler shift and will depend on the speed of the moving source. You can see an example of this with the whistle of a moving train. The train is emitting a sound at a given frequency. As it approaches you, the sound waves are increased in frequency and you can hear a higher pitch; when it is just alongside you will hear the true note of the sound being emitted; as the train recedes, the pitch of the sound will become lower as its frequency is decreased.

This is one example of Doppler shift occurring with acoustic waves. It occurs with any type of wave motion when there is a moving source. By measurements on the light emitted by receding stars, astronomers can calculate how fast the universe is expanding, as shown by the rate at which some of the stars are moving away from us. By measurements on radar waves, the speed of moving vehicles can be checked by bouncing the waves off the moving surface.

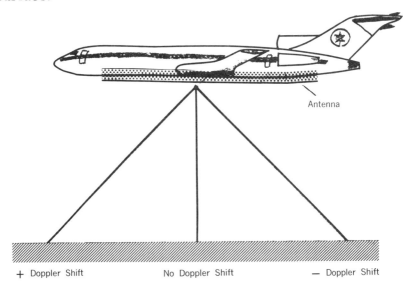

Figure 6.   Doppler Shift of Frequency with a Moving Aircraft.

We will see later that Doppler effects are applicable to problems relating to the reflection of radar waves from aircraft and satellites. On the ground immediately below the craft there is no change in frequency; in the direction of flight the frequency will be increased, while behind it the frequency will be reduced, as Figure 6 shows.

We have been talking about waves and wavelengths. What sort of wavelengths are we concerned with?

Below is shown diagrammatically the spectrum of electromagnetic radiation. It extends from very short wavelengths for gamma rays and x rays up to long wavelengths for radio waves.

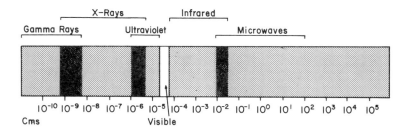

Figure 7. The Electronic Spectrum.

You can see that the part of the spectrum which affects our eyes and which we call light is only a very small part of the whole. On each side of this visible part of the spectrum is an area which is very close to being visible; the threshold between visibility and non-visibility varies from one individual to the next, and some people can see a little further into these regions than others. On the short wavelength side we have the ultraviolet rays. These are the rays which give us a tan in the summer time. At the long wavelength end we have the infrared rays, and they give us the sensation of heat. All of these rays from the gamma rays to radio waves are emitted by the sun, but much of this radiation is absorbed by the earth's atmosphere as it passes through it. This is fortunate for us or we should all have been burnt to a frazzle long ago.

At the moment we are mostly interested in seeing things, and so we will take out the visible part of the spectrum and have a closer look at it. It varies in wavelength from about 400 x 10^{-9} to 750 x 10^{-9} metres (i.e. 4 x 10^{-5} to 7.5 x 10^{-5} cms.)   Since these figures are awkward to cope with, a new unit has been given to this range, and we say that the visible part of the spectrum extends from 400 to 750 nanometres, where a nanometre is 1/1,000,000,000th part of a metre or 1 x 10^{-9} metres.   This is the only part of the vast spectrum of electromagnetic radiation which can be used to transmit messages to our brain through our eyes.   However, camera film is able to record images over a wider range.   It can make use of both the ultraviolet and the near infrared region.   Other types of sensors are capable of detecting even longer wavelengths such as those further out into the infrared, known as the thermal infrared region, and into the microwave region used in radar.

We are used to seeing things in colour. The differences in colour are due to the differences in wavelength of the light reaching our eyes.   Referring to the visible part of the spectrum again, if light with a wavelength of about 450 nanometres strikes the retina behind our eyes, we see a

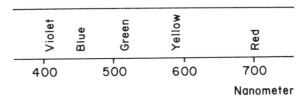

Figure 8.   The Visible Spectrum.

flash of blue light; with a wavelength of about 550 nanometres we see green light; with a wavelength of 700 nanometres we see red light, and so on.   Each wavelength gives a different piece of information when the message reaches our brain.   This explains why different lights give different colours.   A neon light usually appears red because it emits light with a large part of its energy in the range of about 700 nanometres.   Other colours can be created by operating these lamps under different conditions.   Mercury lamps are generally a rather cold blue because most of their radiation is in the violet and blue end of the spectrum at about 400 to 450 nanometres.   (Much of it is also in the ultraviolet, but this we are unable to see).   Sodium lamps used so often around airports are bright orange–yellow because they emit very strongly at about 580 nanometres. Daylight, the light by which we see things out of doors, has a mixture of all these wavelengths or colours so balanced that it appears to have no colour at all, and is therefore called "white" light.

It is possible to describe the colour of light sources by means of curves, and these we call emission curves, in which the relative light intensity at each wavelength is plotted against that wavelength. In Figure 9 (a) shows the emission curve for sodium light which emits very strongly at a little below 600 nanometres and so appears yellow, (b) for a mercury lamp shows very strong emission in the blue and violet, while daylight (c) has a much flatter curve, showing, as we call it, "white" light.

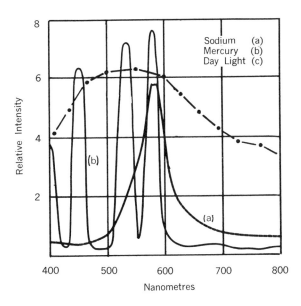

Figure 9. Emission Curves for Light Sources.

As far as natural light sources are concerned, we have first and foremost the sun. The moon we see by reflected light, while the stars we see again by the light which they themselves create. Closer to earth we have a number of less powerful natural light givers such as glow-worms and fire-flies, the microscopic marine animals that give luminance to the waves in the wake of a ship, decaying wood, fungi, and so on. All of these lights can be described by means of emission curves.

We said earlier that we see things by reflected light; we now say that daylight is a "white" light. Why is it that all things seen in daylight do not look white to us? After all, they merely reflect daylight. Why do we see different colours?

The reason is that when white light falls on an object it is not all reflected. The object itself absorbs some of the light of a wavelength depending on the nature of the atoms and molecules of which it is composed.

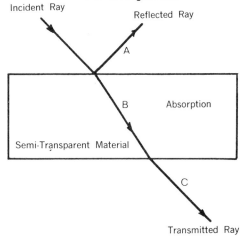

Figure 10. White Light Falling on a Semitransparent Object.

Figure 10 shows what happenes when a beam of light falls on a block of some semi-transparent material such as a piece of coloured plastic. Part of the beam, ray A, will be reflected, while the rest of it, ray B, will travel on; parts of both these rays will be absorbed by the plastic; another part, ray C, will travel right through and come out into the air the other side; it represents the unabsorbed part. It is in the process of absorption that some of the wavelengths are selectively removed. The parts reflected and transmitted are then the complementary colour of that colour which is absorbed. We know that yellow and blue are complementary colours; so are red and green, violet and orange. Let us take a green leaf, for example.   White light containing all wavelengths falls on it, but the chlorophyll in the leaf absorbs those wavelengths corresponding to the red and the blue regions of the spectrum, and reflects only the complementary colour green; so to us a leaf appears green.

So, we say a leaf is green. What sort of green? A bluish green?   A yellowish green?   These descriptions are not precise enough for a scientist. A better way of describing colours is by means of spectrophotometric curves. What is spectrophotometry?   How are these curves derived?   and what will they tell us?

The word photometry derives from two Greek words *photos* meaning "light" and *metron* meaning "measure". Photometry then means the measurement of light intensity. We have light meters on cameras to tell us what exposures to use; we have various light control devices, such as burglar alarms, garage doors which open automatically, and so on, all of which depend on the variation of light intensity. Photo-metry signifies the measurement of the total amount of light although the measuring device, frequently a photocell, may be more sensitive at some wavelengths than at others. It tells us nothing about the distribution of this light over the wavelength bands, or colours. In other words, it tells us nothing about the spectral distribution. This is the science of spectrophotometry. The total amount of light which would reach our eyes is divided up by the spectrophotometer into wavelength bands and the intensity for each particular wavelength is measured.   These

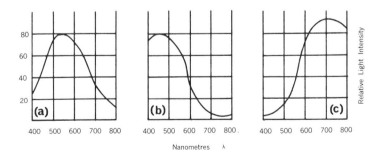

Figure 11. Spectrophotometric Curves for
      (a) Green Surface
      (b) Blue Surface
      (c) Red Surface

intensities can be plotted point by point against the corresponding wavelength to give a curve. By looking at this curve we can tell what colour it represents. Let us look at a series of such curves.

Curves (a), (b) and (c) represent curves for green, blue and red objects respectively. We can see that in (a) there is a high light intensity at about 550 nanometres, in the green range, and so the object appears green. In (b) there is a high intensity at 400 to 500 nanometres, and so the object appears blue. In (c) the peak of intensity appears at about 700 nanometres and so the object appears red.

Thus we are able to describe colours in broad general terms; but spectrophotometric curves can do better for us than this. Take green, for example. Below are two more curves for green. Curve (d) shows a curve for a bluish green and curve (e) shows a curve for a yellowish green. You can see that while both of these peak and have their highest intensity at about 550 nanometres, (d) has more blue light mixed with it, while (e) has more yellow light.

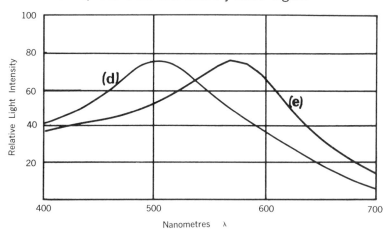

Figure 12. Spectrophotometric Curves for Two Surfaces with Difference Shades of Green.

Although a spectrophotometer is not quite so sensitive as the human eye for the differentiation of colour, quite small colour differences can be distinguished. The green of a coniferous tree such as spruce, for example, is somewhat bluer than the green of a deciduous tree such as maple, and these differences show up well on colour curves. In fact these curves become a sort of fingerprint of a colour, or we can say that any colour has a spectral signature. It is the recording and analysis of spectral signatures that are of particular interest in remote sensing.

The science of spectrophotometry has developed apace during the past half century and has become a valuable tool in industry; among others the textile, paint and paper industries use it for colour matching, and the chemists use it for the analysis of materials. It is so important that it might be of interest to see how in practice these curves are obtained, particularly as the idea behind the method is the basis for many of the remote sensing instruments.

The instrument used for plotting such curves is a spectrophotometer. Its object is to measure the proportion of light reflected (% reflectance) at certain wavelength intervals (at, say, 400, 420, 440, etc. nanometres) from an object whose colour we wish to describe. The first thing to do is to split up or disperse the white light into wavelength intervals or bands. This may be done by a prism or a diffraction grating. Both of these dispersing elements are used on modern instruments, the choice depending on the particular use to which they will be put. We will consider a prism since it is the more familiar object to most people.

It was Isaac Newton, one of the greatest scientists of all time, who first discovered in 1666 that white light is made up of different colours. He did this with a glass prism in a darkened room. He made a small hole in a shutter through

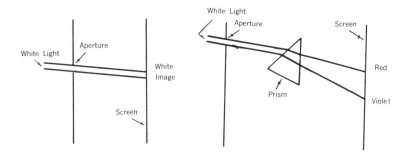

Figure 13. Dispersion of Light by a Prism.

which the sunlight could stream. This ray of white light was allowed to fall on a screen such as you use for home movies and, as would be expected, he saw on this a circular patch of light. Then he placed a prism in the path of the beam between the aperture and the screen, and behold there then appeared a whole series of patches of coloured light, all colours of the rainbow — violet, blue, green, yellow, orange and red (i.e. of wavelengths from 400 to 750 nanometres). At the same time the whole ray had been bent, but the violet ray at one end of the spectrum had been bent considerably more than the red ray at the other end.

In Newton's experiment the coloured images were overlapping, and the colours were confused and very impure, but here was the basis of spectrophotometry. The main aim of researchers since then has been to purify these colours, or to separate out these wavelengths into smaller and smaller bands, or, as a physicist would say, to increase the spectral resolution.

A spectrophotometer used for measuring reflected colour is represented diagrammatically in Figure 14.

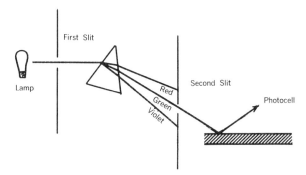

Figure 14. Schematic Diagram of a Simple Spectrophotometer.

Light from a lamp passes through a narrow slit on to a prism, where, as in Newton's experiment, it is split up into its component colours or wavelengths. Another slit is placed in the path of the emerging rays so as to pass just one narrow wavelength band. By moving the slit up and down or by rotating the prism we can select any wavelength band we want. This ray then falls on the object whose colour we wish to measure, and the percentage reflected from its surface is measured by a light-sensitive device, such as a photocell. If we turn the prism, we can select another wavelength and make another reflectance measurement, until the full spectrum of colours has been traversed. By plotting the light intensity as measured by the photocell against the wavelength of incident light, we arrive at a spectrophotometric curve similar to those shown in Figures 11 and 12.

The diagram shown above is simplistic. In fact, there are many optical complications which lead to very sophisticated equipment. Nowadays the values do not have to be read off one by one and plotted manually on a piece of graph paper; the curve may be drawn automatically. Alternatively, figures can be fed into a computer and a full colour description calculated and presented without any visible curve being produced at all.

A full colour curve such as this will allow a full colour description; sometimes, however, it is not necessary to consider a complete curve in order to find out what we want to know. It may be legitimate to make a measurement at one wavelength only, or at two, or even three wavelengths; it really depends on the complexity of the curve. The technique for taking measurements at a few selected wavelengths only is known as abridged spectrophotometry, and it is this abridged spectophotometry which is the forerunner of the multispectral scanners with which we shall be dealing in the next chapter. By making four records, one each in the green and red bands, and two in the infrared band, we can get a great deal of information and establish some simple spectral signatures.

We have discussed two ways in which we see coloured light; one is by direct emission from a light source; the other is by reflection from a coloured object. There is a third way by means of a phenomenon called fluorescence. In this process a material absorbs light of one wavelength, converts it to a longer wavelength and then re-emits it. A material may, for example, absorb blue light and re-emit the energy as green or yellow light; another may absorb green light and re-emit it as red light, and so on. Since light is actually created in the process, fluorescent colours have great purity and brilliance. Some of the bright pinks and reds we see in textiles and on posters are produced by fluorescent dyes and inks.

Of particular interest is a group of materials which absorb the ultraviolet energy we cannot see and re-emit it as visible light. Thus the sum total of light in the Universe is increased. We see the use of such materials in daylight fluorescent lamps. An ordinary mercury vapour light is a cold light containing a high proportion of short wavelengths in the violet and ultraviolet part of the spectrum. A coating of fluorescent powder inside the tube absorbs the invisible rays and converts them to a longer wavelength so that we can see them. This not only gives us a warmer and more pleasing light but leads to greater efficiency, giving us more light for a dollar's worth of power. Another everyday use is in detergents. Most detergents these days contain fluorescent dyes called optical brighteners which tend to adhere to fabrics. When the housewife hangs her washing outside on the line, this dye receives the invisible light from the sun and converts it to a bluish, white light, so that her husband's shirts really will appear, as the advertisements say, "whiter than white". Light has been created within them. Since in our society "whiteness" is considered to be synonymous with "cleanliness", she has the gratification of feeling that the particular brand of washing powder has made her clothes truly clean.

The wavelengths of light absorbed, and the wavelengths of light emitted in the fluorescent process are unique to the particular material involved. The whole mechanism depends on the nature and structure of the atoms and molecules in the material. Since it is caused by molecular configurations, it is reasonable to suppose that materials can be identified by the spectrum of light they produce. This is indeed so. The process provides a method of analysis — one which is particularly applicable to oils. We can quickly differentiate between butter and margarine, for example, and we can detect and identify oil slicks on the ocean. Many geological rocks also show clear fluorescent patterns; so do some factory effluents. The absorption and reradiation of energy takes place ina very short period of time. If a material is briefly illuminated and then the source of illumination removed, the light created will generally disappear very quickly indeed — in a matter of thousandths of a second. Despite its brevity this period of time can be measured, and experimenters have found that the decay time is also a characteristic of a particular material. We thus have three measurable fluorescent characteristics of a substance — the wavelengths which it preferentially absorbs (i.e. its absorp-tion spectrum), the wavelengths of the light which it re-emits (i.e. its emission spectrum) and its decay time. All of these may be used as a means of detection and identifi-cation and will be referred to again in Chapter II in a discussion on lasers.

The phenomenon of fluorescence is brought about by the motion of electrons within the atom. Another phenomenon which also causes a change in the wavelength of light falling on a material is brought about by the motion of the whole molecule. It may vibrate to and fro, or it may rotate, or it may carry out many complicated motions. In doing so it may collide with neighbouring molecules. This was discovered in 1928 by a scientist called Raman and so was called Raman effect. The spectra resulting from these changes of wavelength are called Raman spectra; again they are characteristic of the substances producing them, and can be used to identify them. Raman spectra show up particularly well in gases where the molecules are free to move about, and their use shows great promise for the detection and analysis of air pollutants, such as sulphur dioxide and nitrogen dioxide.

An ordinary light source, such as a lamp or a candle or even the sun, sends out myriads of short trains of waves in all directions. The waves will have different wavelengths and different amplitudes; they will start from different places within the source and will travel in different directions. It is a very higgledy-piggledy and uncoordinated process, and is consequently very inefficient. If now it can be arranged that all these waves have the same wavelength

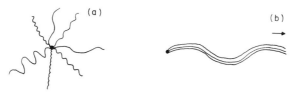

Figure 15. Radiation from a Conventional Light Source (a) and a Laser (b).

and that they be radiated in phase in the same direction, the superposition of so many waves would give a very much greater amplitude and the intensity would be increased enormously. In a laser these conditions can be met, and this is what gives it such a strong and penetrating beam.

The ray as it emerges from the tube is very narrow; its divergence is small. If you have a flashlight and throw a beam of light on a wall about 3 feet away, you know that the light will spread out into a cone; it will diverge and illuminate a circle of wall considerably larger than the circle of light emanating from the flashlight itself. If you move further away from the wall, the circle illuminated will get larger but the light will be fainter. If, on the other hand, you were to illuminate the wall with a laser beam, you would see only quite a small spot of light, perhaps only a few millimetres across, but it would be very intense. As you moved the laser source further away from the wall the spot would remain virtually the same size, because the divergence of the beam is low. Its divergence is so low that is possible to illuminate the surface of the moon with a laser beam from earth, and even at such a tremendous distance the spot of light would only be a mile or so across. Since the beam is so intense, its illuminating effect, even when spread out over so large an area, is still quite strong. We can not only direct a ray of light of this sort on to the moon but we can also receive it back again after reflection. Now, since we know the speed of light, we can send a pulse of light to the moon, receive it back on earth, measure the time it takes to go there and back and so calculate how far the moon is away. This time will be 2 to 3 seconds depending on the position of the moon at the time. The average distance from earth to the moon is 239,000 miles.

The word LASER is an acronym for **L**ight **A**mplification by **S**timulated **E**mission of **R**adiation. This looks like a very complicated and learned phrase, but it isn't really. It merely expresses in a scientist's language what we have already said in simpler terms — that the device is stimulated to emit monochromatic, in-phase radiation so as to amplify the light and give an intense beam. The actual wavelength of light it gives out depends on the materials of which it is made. There is a ruby laser and it may be designed to operate at 694.3 nanometres, giving a red light, and most of its energy will be emitted at exactly 694.3 nanometres. Alternatively there are ways by which the frequency may be doubled (i.e. the wavelength may be halved), so that we can get a wavelength of 347.2 nanometres in the ultraviolet. A carbon dioxide laser may be designed to operate in the infrared region at a wavelength of 10,600 nanometres and it will put out most of its energy at exactly 10,600 nanometres. There is a neodymium glass laser which normally operates at 10,640 nanometres in the near infrared part of the spectrum, but it can be stimulated to emit at half this wavelength, at 532 nanometres. This is in the green part of the spectrum and has an important application in remote sensing systems as will be seen in the next chapter.

We have now considered the reflection and absorption of visible light by earthly objects, and the absorption of invisible ultraviolet rays. We will now go beyond the long wavelength fringe of the visible spectrum to the infrared. There are really two regions here — the optical or near infrared region, which we may consider extends from the edge of the visible range at 750 nanometres up to about 3,000 nanometres, and the thermal or far infrared region which extends from this point up to the microwave range at about 1 millimetre. The actual boundary is quite arbitrary; it is convenient to place it at about this point because for one thing these two areas are used to measure different properties, and for another they require different sensors for their detection. When we discuss the wavelength of infrared radiation, it is generally more convenient to express it in terms of micrometres, (μm) where 1 μm is equal to 10^{-6} metres, so that 1 μm is equal to 1000 nanometres. Therefore, we may say that the near infrared region extends from about 0.75 μm to 3.0 μm, while the far infrared region extends from about 3.0 μm to 1000 μm.

The near infrared waves behave in much the same way as the visible waves we have been discussing. They are emitted by the sun, fall on the earth, are absorbed or reflected, and the intensity of the reflected rays can be measured. The complete record forms part of the spectral signature of an object.

Now let us take a look at the thermal infrared region. This region contains the longer wavelength rays which are responsible for causing heat. All the objects about us, even ice, are emitting infrared rays. We say "even ice" because it is difficult to imagine that ice radiates heat. It all depends on what we mean by heat. Ice does not seem warm to us because our temperature is higher than that of ice, and so comparatively it seems cold, but this is all relative. If you were at the temperature of absolute zero, i.e. at about -273º Celsius or 0º Kelvin, then ice would feel warm (except that at that temperature you would not be able to feel anything at all!) The wavelength at which ice emits infrared radiation is very long; as the temperture of a body rises it emits more radiation, and also the wavelength at which it does so becomes shorter and shorter, so that a spectral curve of such a body tells us quite a lot about its temperature and about its nature. At the average temperature of the earth the radiation peak is at about 10 μ m. If we could see infrared radiation in the same way as we can see visible rays, then warm objects would appear bright while colder objects would seem darker. We cannot see this with our eyes, but we have other "eyes", detectors which can "see" things for us.

The amount of thermal radiation emitted by an object depends mainly on two factors. One is its temperature, as just mentioned; the other is its emissivity. This is a characteristic of the material itself, and indicates the readiness with which the material will give up its heat by radiation. Thus we may have two objects at exactly the same temperature in the same surroundings, but the one with a higher emissivity will radiate thermal rays more strongly than the one with a lower emissivity. The apparent temperature of an object (i.e. the measure of the emitted radiation) is termed brightness temperature. For an object with perfect emissivity the brightness temperature is the same as the true temperature. This is very nearly the case with water.

From any ground object, therefore, we receive two types of infrared radiation — one due to reflected solar radiation in the range of about 750 nanometres, the other due to self-emission of thermal radiation at about 10 micrometres. Fortunately these are so far apart in the spectrum that they can easily be sorted out by using two detectors each sensitive to a different wavelength range. Since the

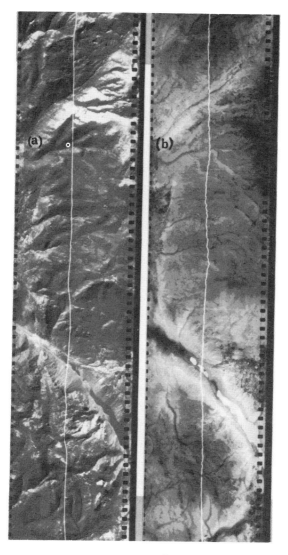

Courtesy of Canada Centre for Remote Sensing

Figure 16. Thermal Infrared Scanner Imagery.
    (a) Taken during the day
    (b) Taken early in the Morning

atmosphere absorbs radiation at 10 micrometres only very slightly, thermal infrared measurements can be made at night and under conditions of haze. This is a tremendous advantage.

One interesting facet of the phenomenon of emissivity and temperature is the difference in the behaviour of land and water. Everyone knows that land cools down at night much more quickly than water, and conversely it heats up more quickly during the day. Consequently, if we obtain an infrared image of a water body such as a lake during the day, the land will be hotter than the water and the lake will appear on a photograph as dark against a lighter background. At night when the land is cooler than the water the same scene will show a light lake against a darker background. This can be seen in Figure 16. (a) represents an infrared image taken during the day. (b) represents the same scene taken early in the morning before the land has had time to heat up. It is interesting to note that the day photograph shows the shadow effect of the mountains very clearly. The south slopes of the mountains warm up more quickly than the northern slopes and so appear darker on a negative print. The white line down the centre represents the flight path of the aircraft.

Moving further out along the electromagnetic spectrum toward longer wavelengths, we come to the microwave region. Again, as before, we find it convenient to change the wavelength unit; we use here the millimetre (mm) or the centimetre (cm), where 1 cm or 10 mm is equal to 10,000 μm. Looking back at the units we have used throughout the spectrum, we see that we started off with nanometres in the visible range, came to micrometres in the infrared range, and now we are in the centimetre region. We can see the necessity for making these changes; if we were still working with nanometres, we would have to be talking about wavelengths of 10,000,000 nanometres instead of 1 cm, which would be awkward. It would be just as if we tried to express the distance from Montreal to Vancouver in inches; we would find it difficult to comprehend the numbers. The range of microwave wavelengths generally used is from about 0.3 cm to about 25 cm.

Another more basic change is often made at about these wavelengths. We know that wavelength is related to frequency in such a way that:

$$f \text{ (frequency)} = \frac{c \text{ (speed of light)}}{\lambda \text{ (wavelength)}}$$

or

$$\lambda = \frac{c}{f}$$

Since the speed of light (or any electromagnetic radiation) is 300,000,000 metres per second, the wavelength can be expressed in metres as

$$\lambda = \frac{300,000,000}{f}$$

The waves in the microwave region are often characterized by their frequency expressed as hertz (hz). This brings them into line with radio waves, to which they are akin, which are generally expressed in megahertz, or megacycles, or millions of cycles per second. A wavelength of 6 cm is equivalent to 5,000,000,000 hz; a wavelength of 0.3 cm is equivalent to about 100,000,000,000 hz. Once again these are inconveniently large numbers to talk about and so they are expressed as 5 Ghz (gigahertz) and 100 Ghz were 1 Ghz is equal to 1,000,000,000 hz or 1×10^9 hz.

As in all other types of radiation, in the microwave range the wavelength dictates the properties and behaviour of the radiation; we can thus designate certain wavelength bands for special purposes. As in the case of the visible spectrum we can say that we have a microwave spectrum. For the sake of convenience letters have been allotted to these bands analogous to the colours of the visible spectrum. Table 1 shows some wavelengths of special interest to us.

Radar is one technique employing microwave radiation; in general we can say that the longer the wavelength the more penetrating is the beam. Radar methods are invaluable for remote sensing under conditions of dark, cloud, fog and rain; even snow and hail may be penetrated if the wavelength is long enough. On the other hand, rain, snow and hail will reflect the shorter wavelength radiation. For this reason remote sensing systems make use of the

Table 1   Wavelength and Frequency Ranges of
Microwave Bands

Range	Wavelength (cm)	Frequency (GHz)
Ka	0.8 to 1.1	40.0 to 26.5
K	1.1 to 1.7	26.5 to 18.0
Ku	1.7 to 2.4	18.0 to 12.5
X	2.4 to 3.8	12.5 to 8.0
C	3.8 to 7.5	8.0 to 4.0
S	7.5 to 15.0	4.0 to 2.0
L	15.0 to 30.0	2.0 to 1.0

longer wavelengths in the X or L bands for obtaining imagery of the earth and sea, while meteorological systems prefer to use the shorter wavelengths for forecasting the weather, storms, etc. L-band radiation is better able to penetrate the surface of ice and is useful in the Arctic regions for telling us something about the nature of this ice.

The ability of an object to be detected and imaged by microwaves depends on its ability to reflect these waves, and this in turn depends on a characteristic known as its dielectric constant. The dielectric constant of a material is related to its ability to conduct electricity. In general, good conductors of electricity such as metals reflect very strongly as a mirror reflects light waves. Water is also a good conductor of electricity, but not quite so good as metals, and so water and wet soil reflect radio waves fairly well; whereas ice, rocks and dry soil are poor conductors and do not reflect so strongly. Different types of rock of different chemical composition reflect to a different degree, and so there is a possibility of seeing differences here which could not be seen at any other wavelength.

We realize that with the exception of thermal phenomena most of the information we get about the earth depends on the reflection of radiation which impinges on it.

The radiation may be visible or it may be invisible, such as near infrared or microwave.

According to the laws of physics a ray falling on to a mirror-like surface is reflected from it in such a way that the angle of incidence is equal to the angle of reflection as shown in Figure 17. One interesting result of this is that if you direct a beam on to two surfaces at right angles to each other, it will, after two reflections, always be reflected back along the same path as it traversed in the beginning but in the opposite directions. Reflectors such as these are called corner reflectors, and there are several practical applications of this principle. The "cat's eyes" down the centre of a road or on warning signs are actually corner reflectors. When a beam from a motorist's headlights strikes them at night the light will be reflected back in the driver's direction. As already mentioned, a laser beam can be directed to the moon and received back again on earth. This was achieved by a corner reflector placed there by one of the moon walkers. Since the walls of buildings are generally at right angles to the road they stand on, strong reflections have been recorded from such constructions by means of microwave beams directed on them from radar systems in aircraft or satellite — a useful aid in interpretation.

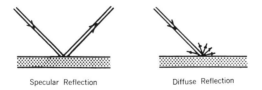

Specular Reflection   Diffuse Reflection

Figure 17. Specular and Diffuse Reflection.

All surfaces, however, do not give such strong directional reflections. The mirror-like reflections we have been describing are the result of specular reflection as shown in Figure 17 (a). On the other hand, if the surface is rough, the beam will be scattered in all directions and only part of it will be sent back in the usual reflected direction, (b). Such behaviour is referred to as diffuse reflection. Freshly fallen snow is an example of an almost perfectly diffusing surface.

In this way the texture of surfaces may be differentiated - of particular significance in interpreting radar images. For example, the state of the oceans, depending on the height of the waves, may be studied in great detail; the nature of vegetation in fields, whether stubble fields, tilled or freshly sown; the regeneration of forest areas and so on.

We can see that in remote sensing we are dealing with radiation over a very broad spectrum from ultraviolet light at less than 400 nm up to microwaves of several centimetres. The properties of these waves and the way they interact with objects they meet are often dependent on wavelength. One other effect we should note is the effect of wavelength on resolution. What do we mean by resolution? Physicists and engineers each have their own way of describing and measuring this property. It is sufficient to say here that it is concerned with the amount of detail we can see. If in a photograph we can distinguish two objects two feet apart but no closer we say that the resolution is two feet. Resolution is better at shorter wavelengths. The resolving power of an instrument using visible light can be considerably better than that of one using microwaves; but, of course, in the design of a system other factors also come into play. In a camera or telescope, for example, the aperture of the lens system is also a factor in determining the resolving power obtainable; in the case of microwave systems the length of the antenna plays an analogous role, but we will see in Chapter III how the disadvantage of long wavelength can be overcome by the design of a synthetic aperture.

We have been discussing the detection of objects on the ground by instruments in the sky. This all depends, of course, on the supposition that radiations sent up from the earth, either by reflection or by emission, actually reach these instruments. Unfortunately not all of them do; some are absorbed on the way by the earth's atmosphere, and high absorption means low transmission. The atmosphere contains a number of gases, many of which absorb quite strongly, even completely at some wavelengths. The visible part of the spectrum shows only slight absorption. However, in the infrared region there are many areas which are virtually useless to us because no rays can get through.

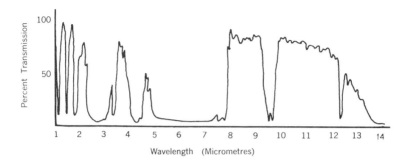

Figure 18. Atmospheric Transmission Spectrum.

Figure 18 shows the atmospheric transmission curve for various wavelengths from 1 micrometre (in the near infrared) up to 15 micrometres. Those positions on the transmission spectrum at which transmission is high are called windows; they allow almost free passage of the rays and the instruments in the air must therefore be designed so that they detect at these wavelengths. At round about 3 μ m, for example, the water vapour and carbon dioxide in the atmosphere absorb very strongly, and again carbon dioxide absorbs at about 5 μ m and water vapour at about 5.5 μ m to 7.5 μ m; these areas must be avoided. On the other hand there are good windows that can be used at about 1.5 μ m and so on. We will be looking at this more closely when discussing the design of sensors in the next chapter.

These then are the general physical principles on which remote sensing methods are based. We will see in the rest of the book how we can apply them and how they can be put to good use by geographers, foresters, agriculturists, engineers and so on.

CHAPTER II

SENSORS - OUR NEW "EYES"

We now understand how it is that we see things and, in particular, how it is that we see things in colour. In brief, light rays, generally emitted by the sun, are reflected by an object into our eyes and so to the retina where they are recorded.

Now we want to design sensors which will not only carry out this "seeing" operation for us but will, if possible, improve upon Mother Nature. This is no easy matter. The eye is a most remarkable instrument. It has virtually a zoom lens which allows it to focus automatically and continuously from a distance of about ten inches in front of our nose right up to infinity. It has an automatically adjustable aperture which allows it to close down under conditions of bright light and open up like a cat's eye in the dark, and it has a very high spectral resolution; in other words it can differentiate very well between different colours, even though they may be very close in shade. Associated with the eye is a human brain which is capable of assimilating and interpreting the messages sent to it. This represents a data-handling system that will be hard to beat in some respects. It is capable of judgement and of memory. However our eyes are limited to using quite a small band in the electromagnetic spectrum, namely the visible range from about 400 to 750 nanometres. Our man-made sensors can extend this range from the ultraviolet wavelengths through the visible and infrared to the microwave region. Each of these different wavelength ranges can contribute something different to our experience and extend our ability to view things.

The instrument closest to the human eye is a camera, and this is really the work-horse for airborne sensing systems (i.e. from aircraft, balloons, etc.). It is understandable that the requirements for sensors for airborne systems are somewhat different from those for satellite systems, especially unmanned spacecraft, where photographic film cannot be brought back to earth for processing. Sensing from aircraft as compared with spacecraft offers many advantages to a sensor designer. For one thing it can afford to be more experimental. We cannot chance putting any equipment into an unmanned satellite unless we are almost 100% sure it will work. Once a satellite has been launched we cannot easily bring it back again to make modifications. With a plane, on the other hand, we can take the risk and try out new ideas; in fact, to some extent we can use aircraft as a research laboratory for the development of sensors which may later be put into satellites.

In spite of many new developments, photography of one form or another is still an important way of finding out about the world we live in, although other systems such as radar, lasers, T.V. cameras and spectrophotometers, are coming into their own.

The instrument for photography is, of course, a camera. While it may seem superficially a somewhat mundane instrument in comparison with some of the more exotic sensors, it is, in fact, a highly developed and sophisticated tool in the hands of an expert. We will not go into the design and principles of cameras or the fundamental mechanisms of photography. This has been well done elsewhere and would need a book by itself, but for anyone interested a list of some of the literature on this subject is given at the end of the book.

The camera is an extremely versatile instrument, and by means of a variety of filter and film combinations and by enhancement techniques during processing, a great deal of information can be obtained by an experienced operator. The difference between the sort of photographs many of us snap on our vacations and the sort resulting from the work of an experienced scientist is as the difference between night and day.

What sort of cameras do we choose for this job? What are the special requirements for an airborne camera? It depends, of course, on what we want to use it for. For survey work and for covering large areas of the ground quickly, a metric survey camera is used, mounted on shock absorbers to minimize vibration. This is a conventional camera which carries a roll of film 25 cm wide and about 61 m long. It gives a standard nine by nine inch photograph.

The amount of ground covered will depend on the height of the aircraft and the type of lens in the camera. The type of lens, that is, the focal length, determines the angle of view, and this together with the height of the aircraft gives the scale of the resulting photograph. The scale number is given by the ratio of aircraft altitude to focal length of lens. If, for example, we are using a camera with a focal length of 6 inches (i.e. half a foot) in a plane flying at 15,000 ft. the scale of the photograph will be $1/2 : 15,000$ or $1 : 30,000$. This assumes that the ground is flat. If not, at the higher points, the scale would be larger. A small scale map means a small sized representation of an area, or a large numerical ratio. Photographs are generally taken with the camera looking vertically down so as to give a plan view of the earth below, although sometimes oblique methods are also used. This is necessary when travelling over the oceans, for example, where there are no landmarks and nothing to relate the vertical to. If a vertical shot is taken, an oblique shot with an auxiliary camera looking at the horizon serves as a check on the attitude of the plane. If oblique photography is used it must always be remembered that the scale will not be uniform across the photo; the distances towards the horizon will be very much compressed. This inaccuracy, however, can be corrected for. Photography for remote sensing is nearly always vertical. Oblique photography is used more for military and surveying purposes. Three cameras are used simultaneously - one in the belly of the plane looking straight down and two oblique cameras mounted one each on the port and starboard sides respectively.

In order to get complete coverage of any area, the aircraft must fly on certain very well-defined paths; these will normally be straight lines. To be sure that there will be no gaps in the coverage if the aircraft happens to veer to the right or to the left, there must be a slight overlap of these paths; this is called sidelap and is generally arranged to be 30%. As the pilot flies along this line, the camera will be operated to take repetitive photographs at specific intervals of time. The interval of time is calculated and normally adjusted to give a 60% "forward" overlap. The reason for this is that when interpreting the photographs afterwards the interpreter may want a stereoscopic view of the area to allow him to see better some of the topo-graphical features. It is generally considered that it is possible to get stereoscopic viewing if there is a forward overlap of successive exposures of at least 50%. It would be cheaper to settle for 50% but just to make sure there are no gaps a figure of 60% is generally chosen. When two overlapping scenes have been obtained they can be mounted side by side in a stereoscopic viewer so that the scene appears three-dimensional. This then is a requirement for an aircraft camera; it must be able to take virtually the same scene repetitively, and the timing mechanism must be accurately set to fire regularly and give the necessary overlap. The time interval will, of course, depend on the speed of the aircraft (V) and its height (H). The ratio (V/H) will have to be calculated. Frequently this is done by a computer device which automatically operates the camera shutter. It is also important that shutter speeds may be fast, particularly when the plane is flying at low altitude or at high speed. Under these conditions the ground objects would be moving fast across the field of view, and unless exposure times were short the image would be blurred.

One of the problems with aircraft is vibration and irregular movement which would affect the resultant photograph if left uncorrected. Special vibration-free mounts must be provided for the camera; gyroscopes combined with torquer motors (autopilot) help to stabilize the planes.

The lens system in these cameras generally has a fairly short focal length of, perhaps, 8 to 30 cm. The film is always placed at the focal length of the lens system so as to give a good focus at infinity. In this way, since an aircraft flies far above the ground, all points on the ground will be in focus and a sharp image will result.

There are other types of cameras also in use. While the large metric camera giving a 25 cm x 25 cm photograph will probably be the mainstay for resource mapping for the near future at any rate, some users are going over to smaller cameras to supplement their programmes. The 35 mm camera is advocated by some. It is more economical in film and the standard picture format of 24 x 36 mm offers the option of two camera positions in relation to the direction of flight, either longitudinal or transverse. Either black and white or colour photographs may be taken and projected on to a standard screen for visual presnetation. By using a suitable overlap between successive frames they also can be viewed stereoscopically. Many landscapes change in the period between major aerial surveys and 35 mm photography can be used very effectively and economically to maintain up-to-date coverage. Also multispectral and multiscale photography may be effected easily and cheaply using multiple mounts for 35 mm cameras.

An intermediate size frequently used is a 70 mm camera. In Canada this is typified by the Vinten camera which gives a photograph 5 cm wide by 5.5 cm long. It has a lens with a very short focal length of about 7.5 cm - 16 cm, a fast shutter speed of 1/700 second, and a film capacity of about 45 metres of film which gives 700 exposures.

These are what you might call the standard cameras for aerial photography. There are others. There is, for instance, a panoramic camera which gives good resolution over a large ground area, but it is rather complicated. The field of vision is small and to achieve good coverage a scanning device must be used to scan across the line of flight; this leads to a variety of mechanical problems. There are, however, some excellent models available that serve a very useful military purpose. Other camera units may carry interchangeable lenses for changing the scale in flight or interchangeable filters for multispectral work.

With all aerial cameras a wide variety of films may be used, and these in turn may be used with a variety of filters. It is in the choice of the film/filter combinations that the hand of the expert really shows. He will know which of these combinations will bring out the features in the image the user is wanting to delineate. He will perhaps use one combination to show up water channels and drainage patterns across the land, another to show up green vegetation, or perhaps to differentiate between healthy and diseased crops, another to show animals or birds, and so on.

Ordinary black and white film is sometimes chosen, sometimes colour film, but one of the most useful and most used films for aerial photography is that known as false-colour film, so-called because, while it gives a colour photograph, the colours will not be the true colours. We will see how this colour-infrared film differs from the ordinary true-colour film that most of us use in our cameras.

Ordinary colour film, as anyone interested in photography probably knows, consists of three coloured layers, each sensitive to a different part of the visible spectrum (see Figure 19). The top layer is sensitive to blue, the middle one to green and the bottom one to red. Since these last two layers are also sensitive to blue light, we must prevent blue light reaching them, and so a yellow filter is interposed between the top layer (blue-sensitive) and the other two. During processing the yellow filter is bleached out, and the dyes developed in the colour layers are complementary to the colour sensitivity of each. The top blue-sensitive layer gives a yellow image of the scene, the green-sensitive layer gives a magenta (purple) image, and the red-sensitive layer gives a cyan (blue-green) image. This can be used *as is* if we are wanting only to delineate boundaries, or the colours can be reversed by the next stage of the process to give the true colours that we normally expect to see in a colour transparency.

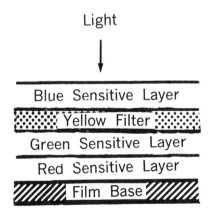

Figure 19. Conventional Colour Film.

These natural colour films have an important place in aerial photography, but they have several disadvantages. The light path from the ground to the plane is a long one, and if there is much haze some of this light gets scattered or absorbed, particularly at the blue end of the spectrum. The resulting pictures will probably be indistinct, even if a haze filter is used.   Also when using ordinary film, either black and white or colour, we are not making use of all the radiation available.   Infrared rays also are reflected by objects on the ground, and they are capable of giving us a great deal of information; they have a better ability to penetrate haze than those associated with the shorter wavelengths.   Colour-infrared film makes use of these near infrared wavelengths.

As in the case of ordinary colour film the colour-infrared film, sometimes called camouflage detection film, is made up of three layers.   However, there the similarity ends; the layers are different.   There is no blue-sensitive layer; this is replaced by a near infrared layer, so that we have a green-sensitive layer, a red-sensitive layer and an infrared-sensitive layer as may be seen in Figure 20.

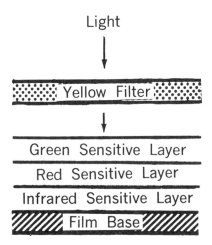

Figure 20. Colour Infrared Film.

The problem now becomes, if we want to develop the colours of the film after exposure, what do we do about the infrared? If is difficult to portray a colour we cannot see. This problem is solved by forgetting about the true colours altogether and replacing them with others. As a result green is portrayed on the finished film as blue, red is portrayed as green and infrared becomes red. Healthy vegetation, which appears to us to be green, will appear on the film as red because it reflects infrared so strongly; unhealthy plants, whether the cause of their ill-health be drought, disease, or insects, will appear bluey-green and so may be easily differentiated from the red colour of healthy plants. With this film we must again use a yellow filter to prevent blue light from entering the camera. Now we can see why it is called camouflage detection film. While ordinary camouflage film using near infrared radiation to give a black and white image has been used for many years, this colour-infrared film was really brought to its present state of refinement during the Viet Nam war. The enemy wishing to camouflage tanks, gun emplacements, etc., in a forest area would cut down branches of trees to cover these objects and hide them from view. Ordinary black and white film or even colour film would not show up these positions, but take a photograph with colour-infrared film and the dying branches would show up clearly. Not only can the healthiness and vigour of plants be detected, but it is also possible to distinguish between coniferous and deciduous trees, and to measure the extent of such forests.

Water does not permit the reflection of infrared rays, and so it appears black, in sharp contrast to any land with which it is in contact. Colour-infrared film seems to be the best for urban applications and city planning. In fact, the applications for infrared film are legion, and new developments are unfolding all the time. These will be dealt with more fully in Chapters VII, VIII, and IX, where we will look at the uses of remote sensing.

Instead of passing all the light from a scene through a single lens on to a composite film with layers sensitive to green, red and infrared rays as we have just discussed, we can get the same effect by splitting up the light with filters into these same three colour bands and passing them separately into three separate cameras. These cameras will

carry ordinary black and white film, but one camera will
photograph a scene through, perhaps, a green filter, another
through a red filter and the third through an infrared filter.
These scenes must be identical. The cameras must therefore be very accurately aligned and the shutter mechanisms
must be arranged to open and expose the films at exactly
the same time. When we realise that exposure times may be
of the order of 1/700 second, this is no mean requirement.
The shutter mechanisms will have to be fired very rapidly,
particularly when flying at low level if we want a 60%
overlap of scenes for stereoscopic viewing. The result of
these three simultaneous exposures will be three black and
white transparencies of the same scene which will differ
only in gradations of density or greyness depending on the
colour of light reflected from the ground scene. (When we
say "colour" we are considering infrared as a colour, even
though we cannot see it.) In a way, we might say that we
are back again to the same situation as with the colour-
infrared film with its three separate colour sensitive layers.
But this latter method with the three separate cameras is
somewhat   more   flexible.   We   can   vary   the   filter
combination, and we can vary the way in which we present
the final picture.

Often the user will be able to examine the three original
black and white negative transparencies *as is* without any
subsequent enhancement. By comparing the densities of the
films obtained in the three different colour bands, he may
be able to get all the information he wants. Some users
prefer to do it this way because they feel that by further
processing some of the resolution is lost and the detail is not
so clear.

On the other hand, we can get either a true or a false-
colour image from three black and white films if we want it.
The colours we get will depend on the choice of filters and
method of processing.

Supposing we want a true colour representation. We
would have to use a blue, green or red filter with cameras 1,
2, or 3 respectively. After exposure we would have three
transparencies. These would be negatives, but we could
reverse them to yield positive transparencies if we wanted
to. By illuminating them with blue, green, and red light
respectively, and projecting the images on to a screen so

that they are exactly superimposed, we would see the scene in natural colours. It works this way: Imagine a simple ground scene of three squares, one blue, one green, and one red, as depicted in Figure 21(1).

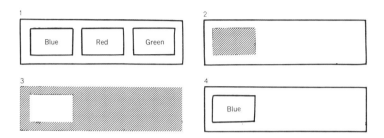

Figure 21. Production of Coloured Images using Black and White Film.

If this scene is photographed by the three cameras each with a blue, green, or red filter on black and white film, the scenes will all look different; the camera with a blue filter will give a negative after development which shows the blue square as dark on a transparent piece of film (2). A positive transparency of this will be light against a dark background (3). If now you project this on to a screen using a blue projection light you will see a blue square again as in the original ground scene (4). Repeating this with the other two colours for the other two cameras and superimposing all these images on the screen will allow you to build up a picture in natural colours exactly as you would have seen it from the plane. You may now photograph the screen using ordinary colour film and the result would be just the same as if you had taken a colour picture from the plane in the first place. You may say "Why go to all that trouble then? Why didn't you use a colour film in the first place?" The answer is that with the more indirect method you can be much more flexible in presenting the final composite image. When projecting the transparencies you can use a variety of coloured lights with different intensities, and can experiment until you see the best discrimination of detail.

In exactly the same way we can build up a colour-infrared image. The camera will have the green, red, and infrared filters corresponding to the layers in the composite film, and again this will produce positive or negative black and white transparencies as we choose. Again we can illuminate these transparencies with any coloured lights to show up the detail we wish to see. If the positive transparencies resulting from the green, red, and infrared filters are projected on the screen with blue, green, and red light respectively, we once again arrive at the same result as is given with a colour-infrared film. Alternatively we can use any other combination of colours.

You can see from all this that the possibilities of combining these techniques are legion. They show what a very versatile tool photography can be.

When man set out on his journey into space it was natural that he should want to make a photographic record of this, his greatest adventure. The early astronauts carried fairly conventional small cameras, with both black and white and colour film and they took some beautiful shots. These were mostly taken at an altitude of 160-320 km and showed surprisingly good resolution. Most of us have seen some of these, particularly those from the Gemini series of spacecraft. In a later mission, that of the Apollo-Saturn 4 unmanned satellite (Nov., 1967), some splendid views of the whole earth were obtained from a height of about 13,680 km. The colours of the early photographs were a little difficult to interpret because we had had no experience of what our earth looked like from outer space. During travel through the atmosphere some of the light rays are absorbed and scattered - some wavelengths more than others - and so the colours are to some degree changed. However these photographs, while they may not have had too much scientific value, demonstrated beyond doubt that the taking of photographs from space held great promise. They were important in that they pointed the way of the design of sensors in subsequent projects. It was with the launching of satellites to orbit the earth at regular intervals over long periods of time that space imagery came into its own. For the first time we were able to obtain images of parts of the earth sequentially, taking shots of the same scene time and time again on a repetitive basis over the months and years; we were able to watch the changing features of our environment. Such has been the case with weather satellites, with Landsat and, more recently, with Seasat.

Instead of taking photographs with conventional cameras, it is generally more convenient in unmanned satellites to use other forms of sensors, where we can relay the data to earth on a *real time* basis. This means that we can receive the pictures at the moment the satellite passes over the scene. Alternatively the images may be stored in the spacecraft by recording them on a tape, and then transmitted later to earth on command from a ground control station.

For this purpose television cameras can be used. One common type of T.V. camera is the vidicon. Its essential component is a photoconducting screen. A photoconducting material is one whose electrical conductance varies with the intensity of light falling on it. A scene to be televised is focused by a lens system on to such a screen which is capable of storing the picture for a period of about 1/10th of a second. During that time a beam of electrons is shot on to the back of the screen and made to sweep across it from side to side in a raster pattern as in Figure 22.

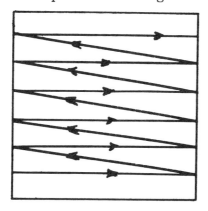

Figure 22. Scanning Pattern for T.V. Camera.

These lines have been drawn wide apart to make the diagram clear; in fact in a T.V. camera there will be about 525 of these horizontal lines, and the scanning process is so fast that the whole face of the screen is covered almost instantaneously. Since this is a photoconducting surface, the magnitude of the current will vary as the amount of light falling on the screen, a bright light giving rise to a high electric current. As this sweeping action progresses, the beam actually has the effect of sweeping the picture off the face of the vidicon in much the same way as we might erase a pattern line by line on a blackboard. In effect, we have now broken the picture up line by line into myriads of little pieces. Fortunately, unlike Humpty Dumpty, it can be put back together again elsewhere. This is what is done by the picture tube in our T.V. set. The pieces in the form of an electric current of varying intensity are transmitted in some way and used to modulate a signal to a cathode ray tube in the receiver of a T.V. set. Here a spot of light is focused on a screen. The brightness of this light is dependent on the magnitude of the current, the larger the current the brighter the light. The spot of light is then swept across the screen in a raster pattern as before and in synchronism with the original electron beam. A picture is thus built up on the screen exactly like the picture we broke down before. The whole process is so fast that our eyes do not see the spot of light travelling across the screen, except when the set is not working properly and then we are aware of the series of horizontal lines during scanning.

This is the basis of television. The current from the vidicon may be led by means of cables directly into a receiver in the room next door, and so we have closed-circuit television. It enables medical students sitting in their classroom to watch an operation being performed in another part of the hospital; it enables a nurse in a central office to keep a close watch on a number of patients at the same time, a supervisor in industry to monitor factory processes, and so on. Alternatively the current from the vidicon may be led to an antenna and so transmitted by radio waves to any part of the world. Thus we were able to see the far side of the moon and watch the astronauts take their first walks in space - all from a comfortable armchair.

The camera just described is similar to the one that was used in the Tiros series of weather satellites. However, there is one important difference. The vidicon cameras used in satellites require a higher resolution. What does this mean ? It means that we need to be able to see more detail; we need to be able to break our picture up into smaller pieces. When an earth scene is imaged from so far away, the scale is very small and unless the resolution is good the picture would be nothing but a blur. To go back to the analogy of the eraser and the blackboard, it means that we would need a very small eraser and would have to traverse the scene many more times in order to clean the board. In the same way, in order to get higher resolution in a vidicon we have to design one in which the electron beam sweeping across the screen has a very small cross-section; to erase the picture it will then have to make many more passes to and fro - between 4,000 to 5,000 as against 525 for a T.V. camera.

A slight modification to an ordinary vidicon camera has given us the Return Beam Vidicon (RBV), which is at present being used in our resource satellites. The advantages of this over the standard type are a higher sensitivity, a better signal-to noise ratio, and a higher resolution. Perhaps we should explain some of these terms. Sensitivity is almost self-explanatory; it means the camera is very responsive to light and can take photographs at low light levels. Signal-to-noise ratio means the degree to which an object stands out against its background, while resolution, as just described, relates to the amount of detail we can see. In the ordinary vidicon camera the electron beam scans the surface on which the scene is focused, and the resulting current is led to a signal electrode. In the Return Beam Vidicon the electron beam scans the surface as before but is then reflected back into a photomultiplier section, where it is amplified and transmitted to earth.

The first two earth resource satellites (Landsat 1 and Landsat 2) carried three RBVs with three different filters (green-blue, yellow-red and near infrared) to provide three black and white records for producing colour-infrared images as already described. Each picture covered an identical area of ground 185 km square with a resolution of 79 m. It gave an image 25 cm x 25 cm with a scale of 1:1,000,000. However experience showed that coloured images could be better produced by the Multispectral Scanner System (details below), while the RBV showed more promise for structural detail. The instrument was therefore modified to record panchromatic images only for the spectral range from 500 nm to 750 nm. At the same time the image was enlarged to give better spatial resolution. In fact, the camera covered only one-quarter of the field of view covered by the original RBVs. In Landsat 3 two such cameras are mounted side by side and together they sweep a path on the ground 182 km wide. Since each individual camera provides the data for an area of ground 98 km x 98 km with a resolution of 40 m, there is an overlap across the track of 14 km, which makes possible its use for stereo viewing.

The **Return Beam Vidicon** (RBV) represents one class of sensors included in the Landsat package. Another is represented by the multispectral scanner (MSS), which differs from the RBV in its scanning mechanism and pre-sentation.

Instead of focusing a ground scene through a camera lens on to a film or, in the case of the RBV, on to a screen, and then scanning the screen, we can scan the ground directly. This data can then be transmitted to earth (or *telemetered*, as the satellite people say) where it is received and converted into an image.

In order to understand how a multispectral scanner works, we must now think back again to the spectro-photometer we looked at in Chapter 1. You remember we saw that the colour of any object can be described by a reflectance curve, in which the intensity of reflected light is plotted against wavelength. This curve gives the spectral signature of an object. We also saw that for simple curves, such as we generally obtain for light which has been reflected, it is not always necessary to draw the full curve; we can often get all the information we want from one or two readings taken at specific places on the curve. This is virtually what is done with a multispectral scanner.

The MSS works by scanning a swath of the terrain below the spacecraft. It does not take an instantaneous snapshot as does the RBV but sweeps the scene as the spacecraft moves over the earth so that finally a continuous picture is built up line by line. Figure 23 shows how it works.

The satellite itself travels from North to South and views a strip of terrain 185 km wide, while the mirror scans across this strip from West to East. Light from the ground is received by the mirror and reflected through an optical system on to a fibre optics array containing 24 elements. We will look at the reason for this. The radiation from earth is picked up from a strip of land perpendicular to the

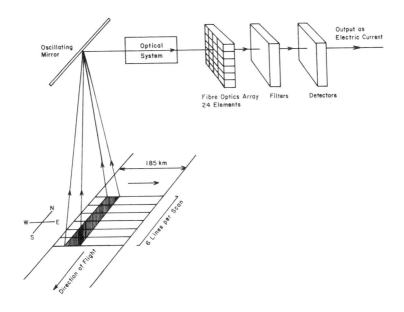

Figure 23. Schematic Diagram of the Multispectral Scanner.

direction of flight. This strip is rather wide; consequently
the resolution would be poor and we should lose a lot of
detail. To avoid this the beam when received by the fibre
optics array is split into 6 parts and impinges on 6 different
strips of elements. This will then have the same effect as if
we were scanning the terrain in 6 narrow strips across the
direction of flight instead of 1 wide one and so will improve
the resolution. We want to do this for each of the four
wavelength bands. Each of these 6 array elements is
therefore split into 4, giving 24 elements in all. The light
from each of these elements is passed through a filter
corresponding to one of the wavelength bands, and then on
to one of a bank of 24 detectors. All of these have the
ability to change a light signal into an electric signal, but
they differ from each other in having different
photosensitive surfaces; 6 of them will be sensitive to
wavelengths 500 to 600 nanometres (band 4); 6 of them will
be sensitive to wavelengths 600 to 700 nanometres (band 5);
6 of them to wavelengths 700 to 800 nanometres (band 6),
and the remaining 6 to wavelengths 800 to 1,100 nanometres

(band 7). Detectors for bands 4, 5, and 6 are photomultiplier tubes, while band 7 is detected by a silicon photodiode.

Once again we have transformed light signals from earth into electric signals which, after being modified by suitable electronic gadgetry, can be instantly telemetered to earth in real time. Alternatively, they can be recorded on tape on board the spacecraft and telemetered to earth later on command from a ground station.

Now we saw that the original RBV cameras taking a snapshot type of image covered an area of ground 185 km square. The MSS is recording images along a continuous strip of land 185 km wide. This is not a very convenient form for making photographic reproductions. Arrangements are therefore made to chop these records up electronically in such a way as to give eventually a scene of a piece of earth similar to that provided by the RBV. The final output from the MSS will therefore be images of terrain 185 km square in each of 4 wavelength bands. Although the scanner sweeps across the track continuously, it does not record a continously variable signal (analogue). It records values element by element across the track (digital), taking about 3240 readings in all. Each instantaneous reading is taken on an element of ground 57 m in width. Along track the width of each of the six strips is 79 m. Eventually therefore our picture will be built up of small elements 79 m x 57 m. Each of these small elements is called a *pixel*.

You may wonder why two sensing systems so similar as the RBV and the MSS, both covering the same area of ground and both operating over approximately the same wavelength range, were used in this satellite. You must remember that Landsat 1 was an experimental satellite; its primary function was not to gather data so much as to see if such a system would be feasible, and we did not know quite how these sensors would behave under conditions of flight. The RBV system has a resolution higher than that of the MSS. It is taking instantaneous snapshots, but the MSS system is operating continuously and so is subject to possible errors owing to motion of the spacecraft in its flight. It was therefore expected that the RBV images would give better clarity and resolution than those of the MSS. In fact the MSS behaved much better than had been expected and gave excellent pictures as may be seen in Plates III and IV. When soon after launch the RBVs had to be deactivated because of problems with their power supplies, almost all the data had to be sent from the scanning system.

Comparing results from the two sensors, it can be said that the RBV system with its analogue recording was the better for mapping where good resolution at a single wavelength band was needed. The MSS system was the better for giving data for colour composites; also since the data from this sensor was sent to earth in digital form it was the only one suitable for quantitative evaluation. It was advantageous for the production of computer compatible tapes, which could in turn be used in various image analysis systems.

This was the reason why in Landsat 3 the RBV system was modified for the sole purpose of providing black and white pictures of good resolution, while the MSS was maintained for the special purpose of providing data for colour images and for computer compatible tapes.

We will see in Chapter VI how the data from the MSS can be used to classify spectral signatures and arrive at a thematic map. This should be of special interest in classifying agricultural scenes, and is of such importance that a thematic mapper has been included in the Landsat-4 package launched in 1982.

The multispectral scanner as used in aircraft and spacecraft has proved invaluable and will no doubt be used with perhaps minor modifications in satellites for many years to come. However, scientists are never satisfied, and it seems that no sooner do they bring one instrument into operation than they are seeking improvements. The next stage of development was directed at improving the radiometric sensitivity and the spectral resolution and flexibility. A better radiometric sensitivity would enable readings to be made at lower light levels; this would be particularly advantageous over bodies of water, where the reflected light in the direction of the sensors is sometimes very low, at high latitudes with low sun elevation angles and in cases of fluorescence detection, where again there is a minimum of light intensity. Greater spectral flexibility would enable users to change the spectral ranges to suit their particular problems rather than having to accept the limitations imposed by the fixed ranges of the multispectral scanner.

Several types of improved instruments have been developed, in which many detectors are used to improve light detection sensitivity. One of these, the Optical Multi-channel Analyser (OMA), developed at C.C.R.S. for aircraft, has 500 detector elements on which the spectrum is dispersed giving very high spectral resolution. The light received is dispersed by a spectrometer prism or grating, and each spectral band falls on a separate detector. A light pipe pointing to the sky measures the downward falling radiation, while the downward pointing spectrometer measures the radiation reflected upward from ground objects. This data is recorded on a magnetic tape in the aircraft. A computer is later able to compensate for variations in the daylight and can also take into account changing effects due to atmospheric absorption and scattering. The end result is a measure of the reflectance of the ground at 500 different wavelengths. Since it is possible to narrow the band pass to only two nanometres, a very detailed and characteristic spectral signature is produced. One particular application of this OMA system is to the colour of rivers, lakes and seas where slight variations in colour are significant in a study of water quality, chlorophyll and turbidity. The OMA does not provide images as do the other sensors we have been discussing, but instead gives a profile of reflectance values along the straight line path below the aircraft. The path does not necessarily have to be immediately below the aircraft; it may be at any angle from 50° forward to 30° back. The track width depends on the height of the aircraft,

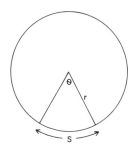

Figure 24. Definition of a Radian.

but it corresponds to an angular width of about 2 milliradians.

Since the term "radian" expressing an angular measurement will be used several times throughout this book, we should perhaps define it for those who are unfamiliar with it.

In Figure 24 the angle θ at the centre of the circle of radius r is equal to 1 radian, when the length of the arc s is equal to the radius. We then may say that

$$\theta = \frac{s}{r} \text{ radians}$$

We therefore see that 2 milliradians (θ = 2/1000 radian) would give a value for s of 2/1000 x r. In the case of an aircraft flying at 3,000 m, for example, the width of the track on the ground (s) would be about 2/1000 x 3,000, or about 6 m. At 30,000 m the width of the track would be about 60 m and so on.

A complete study of all the spectral detail in the OMA data would require 500 traces (i.e. one for each waveband) - all recorded on magnetic tape in the aircraft. What a blessing we have computers ! Even so the handling of so much data is a major task; without computers it would be impossible. Of course, it is not always necessary to get data for all 500 wavebands, if we know which particular band is of most interest. For example, spectrophotometer curves derived from *in situ* measurements on actual water samples collected from Lake Ontario, have been carried out by the Canada Centre for Inland Waters. A statistical analysis of these results and of field tests from aircraft have given some information on the best spectral bands to use for diagnosing certain impurities in water. The application of these methods to the study of water quality will be discussed further in Chapter VIII - Rivers, Lakes and Seas. Although the OMA does not by itself give an image, it provides useful data for detailed spectral studies, and for the selection of sites which can then be scanned later by an imaging instrument.

In imaging instruments the demands for greater radiometric sensitivity and spectral flexibility have been met by the design of a new instrument known as a **Multidetector**

Electrooptical Imaging Scanner (MEIS). We saw how in the multispectral scanner an oscillating mirror swept across the track to gather data from one small element of ground after another. Each small element is called a pixel and it is the size of these pixels which determines the spatial resolution; the smaller the pixel, the better is the resolution. However, if the pixel is too small the amount of light sent back to the instrument is too small to be measured. The MEIS gets over this difficulty by making use of many detectors and electrooptical rather than mechanical scanning. This is known as a *push-broom* scanner. The great advantage is that instead of using a single detector for each waveband for all the pixels across the track, as is done in the MSS, and directing the radiation to the detector from each pixel in turn, there is one detector for each pixel and the whole width of the track is sampled at the same time. As the aircraft moves forward, the whole track is swept, so to speak - hence the name "push-broom". Thus each detector is able to devote the whole of its time to one small element of ground. In the first protype MEIS there was an array of 512 detectors for each of two wavebands so arranged as to "look at" 512 pixels across the track simultaneously. The detectors integrate all the energy reaching them until they are sampled on a repetitive basis, and the data transferred pixel by pixel to a tape recorder. Along the track data from adjacent pixels is given by the movement of the aircraft. This arrangement leads to a very much higher radiometric sensitivity, and this in turn enables smaller pixels to be measured, thus giving better spatial resolution. A second generation MEIS is under development for use in aircraft, which will have arrays of 1728 detectors and eventually up to 8 spectral bands. The fact that there are no rotating parts leads to good geometric accuracy because each pixel

---

A somewhat similar system has been developed for use in aircraft at the Institute of Ocean Sciences in Victoria, B.C. and will be discussed in Chapter VIII. The Coastal Zone Colour Scanner carried by the satellite Nimbus-7 and specially designed for the quantitative determination of chlorophyll and sedimentation will also be discussed in this chapter.

is in a fixed position with the respect to every other pixel in the solid state detector array; there is no shifting of position as the mirror is swept from side to side of the track. This will be of particular importance for mapping.

MEIS uses lenses for focussing the light from the ground on to detectors, and each detector has its own lens. In the original model there were thus 512 element detector arrays with one lens for each array. Ideally the focal lengths of these lenses should be perfectly matched. However, since perfection is seldom achieved, the best selection is made and then any minor errors are corrected. In the same way any non-uniformity of detector sensitivity must also be compensated for. Corrections can be made by means of appropriate mechanisms in the aircraft so as to give realtime corrected imagery. The fact that each detector has its own lens gives a spectral flexibility which would not otherwise be possible, since we can put any filter we choose in front of each lens/detector combination. It will be feasible, for example, to match up any of the colour combinations in a satellite, so that an aircraft flying underneath will be able to gather information in support of that satellite.

We can see that from the relatively simple instruments first launched in Landsat I, developments are taking place which will lead to much greater sophistication and complication. There is a trend to narrower spectral bands and smaller pixels, and the greater versatility will enable more scope for designing instruments for special purposes.

The systems we have been considering so far are called *passive* systems. The sensors record the intensity of electromagnetic waves which are reflected or emitted from the earth. These may be rays which were originally emitted by the sun and merely reflected by ground objects, or they may be thermal rays emitted by ground objects themselves because of their temperature. The main point is that the sensors did nothing about providing any of this energy; they merely received and recorded it. Their role was a passive one.

Now we are coming to *active* systems in which the aircraft or spacecraft itself provides the energy for "illuminating" the earth, and this energy is later reflected back into its sensor. This might be likened to conventional photography when you use a flash bulb. Photography with a flash, we might say, is an active system; photography without a flash is a passive system.

There are two classes of active systems at present in use. One of these involves the use of lasers, which we will consider now; the other involves the use of microwaves, which we will look at in the next chapter.

As we saw in Chapter I, a laser produces a narrow, monochromatic beam of very high intensity and so is particularly suitable for illuminating the ground from a distance, such as an aircraft at an altitude of about 1,500 m. A typical beam divergence would be 2 milliradians; this means that at a height of 1,500 m - the usual operating altitude - the spot of light on the ground would be 3 m in diameter. If now a pulse of laser light is sent out from a plane and is reflected back again from the ground, we can measure the time it takes to travel there and back and so calculate the height of the plane. Alternatively, if the altitude of the plane is known, we can measure the topography of the terrain below. This is the basic principle of LIDAR, which is an acronym for Light Detection And Ranging. Since lidar is an active system providing its own light, it can be operated day and night; in fact, it is sometimes preferable to work at night since the signals being returned would be free of any spurious reflections of sunlight.

This technique can be used for measuring very accurately the height and disposition of ridges in sea ice; knowledge of this nature is of great interest to glaciologists studying ice formation in Arctic waters. It can also be used over earth for recording profiles of hilly terrain. If the aircraft is flown at a constant height along a prescribed path, the height of the land immediately below it may be determined by timing the light signals reflected from it.

The use of lidar systems for measuring range has been an established practice with the U.S. military for some years. Neodymium glass lasers operating at 1.06 micrometres in the infrared part of the spectrum have the advantage of being invisible to the enemy, and have been fitted to missiles, helicopters, tanks, etc.

The system can, of course, also be used in reverse, so to speak, by lasers operating from earth and reflected by a plane or satellite. This has been done by the U.S. Geological Survey in a study to determine the movement of large land masses over the earth's crust. Two laser stations were installed, one in San Diego and the other in Quincey, California, and their beams were directed at a mirror system carried on board a satellite, Lageos, orbiting 3,600 miles above the earth. Over a two-year period they found that these two cities had shifted nearly four inches along the San Andreas fault.

One application for which laser techniques are proving particularly suitable is the measurement of depth of shallow waters. As might be expected, this is of interest to the Armed Forces in connection with the landing of craft on enemy coasts. In Canada it is being investigated with great success for the measurement of water depths in coastal areas, lakes, and rivers. A special instrument called a *Laser Bathymeter* has been built for this purpose for the Canada Centre for Remote Sensing.

We know that the best wavelength to use for the penetration of water is in the green part of the spectrum; so the laser in the bathymeter is a pulsed frequency-doubled neodymium laser operating at a wavelength of 532 nm. It is carried in a plane, and, as Figure 25 shows, a pulse of light is directed downward on to the water. Part of this is reflected back to the receiver in the plane, while part travels through the water and is reflected back again off the bottom. The receiver will therefore detect two pulses, one from the surface of the water and one from the bottom. These light pulses are transformed into electric pulses and may be recorded on magnetic tape for subsequent study or displayed in real time on a cathode ray tube. Either method will allow us to measure the time interval between the reception of the two pulses. This in turn will allow us to calculate the extra distance travelled by the second pulse, and therefore the depth of water. Since the beam has to travel through the water and back again, the depth of water, D, will of course be half of the extra distance travelled. Since the speed of light in water is less than it is in air, we must take this into consideration. If we call this speed s, and difference in the arrival time of the pulse t, we can say that:

$$D = \frac{s \times t}{2}$$

These time intervals are very short, of the order of nanoseconds, that is fractions of a millionth part of a second.

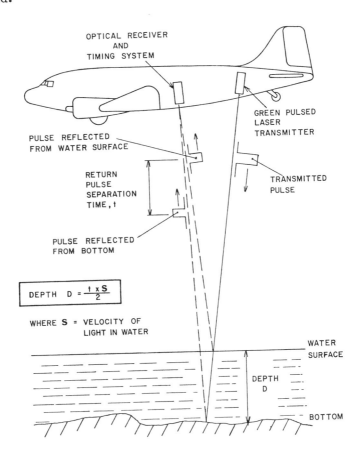

Figure 25. Principle of Operation of Airborne Laser Bathymetric System.

The depth of penetration obtainable depends, of course, on the clarity of the water. The clearest waters in the western hemisphere are in the West Indies, and here it is possible to measure under ideal conditions depths of several hundred feet. Canadian waters are less favorable, particularly near the coasts where water is more turbid, but the method is generally considered to be suitable for depths up to about 30 feet. It is being extensively used by the Canadian Hydrographic Service for charting the coastal waters around Newfoundland and the Arctic, as will be discussed further in Chapter VIII. Similar systems are being developed in the U.S. and Australia.

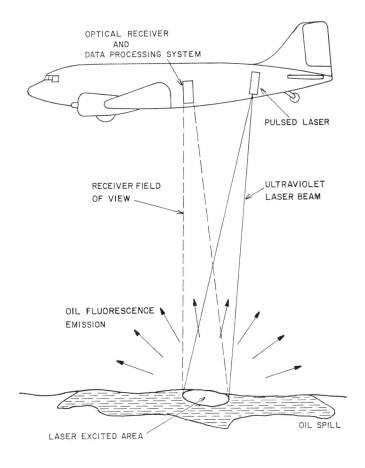

Figure 26. Principle of Operation of Airborne Fluorosensing System.

There is another active system involving the use of lasers, which works on an entirely different principle. We saw in Chapter I that some materials fluoresce; they absorb light at one wavelength, frequently in the ultraviolet, and re-emit it at a longer wavelength. The wavelength of this reradiated light is specific to the material concerned and so can be used to identify it. Oils are examples of materials which fluoresce very strongly and different oils re-emit their energy at different wavelengths. If, therefore, we illuminate the ocean with light of a known wavelength and find on its return that this wavelength has changed, we will be able not only to detect oil spills but also perhaps to identify the type of oil and so trace the source. Figure 26 shows how this may be done. In some ways this system is a little more complicated than the bathymeter in that it is not sufficient merely to detect the return signal; we have to analyze its spectrum.

The instrument for carrying out this spectral analysis is called a fluorosensor. The present model as developed for the Canada Centre for Remote Sensing uses a nitrogen laser giving an excitation wavelength of 337 nm in the ultraviolet. The receiver looks at the illuminated spot on the water and analyzes the spectra of the returning light. It is able to break the light up into spectral bands ranging from 380 nm to 700 nm. The first channel is centred at 381 nm where the Raman line for water occurs. At this wavelength there will normally be a signal from the water surface; if, however, there should be a layer of some other material, such as oil, over the water the signal would be suppressed. The next 14 channels from 400 nm to 600 nm are each 20 nm wide and serve to analyze the returning fluorescent spectrum; the sixteenth channel is centred at 685 nm in the red part of the spectrum and is used to detect the presence of chlorophyll by its own characteristic fluorescence spectrum. All of this data is passed in digital form to the data acquisition system in the aircraft. A lidar system is also incorporated in the fluorosensor package and it records the altitude of the plane; this allows the returning signal to be corrected for plane height. Corrections for a number of other factors are also fed into the computer and the final result is displayed on a TV-type tube. At the same time a record is made on a computer-compatible tape to enable further study at a later date.

Further developments in the design of the fluorosensor are continuing. Other lasers more powerful than the nitrogen laser are now available which will improve the detection limits and will, we hope, give better discrimination between different types of oils. The use of a scanning system would allow a wider swath to be imaged and this, in turn, would mean that a larger area could be monitored more quickly.

Although most of the preliminary work with the fluorosensor has been done in connection with oil spills and the oceans, these techniques can also be applied to the land and inland waters. Some minerals fluoresce and the geologists are watching these developments with interest. The method may assist in some agricultural studies because chlorophyll is a natural material which has a fluorescent spectrum.

Experiments carried out with the co-operation of a pulp mill at Hawkesbury, Ontario, on the Ottawa River, showed that fluorescent measurements from aircraft can be used very effectively for the monitoring of effluents from pulp and paper mills. During the cooking of the wood some materials, called lignosulphonates, are extracted and pass with the spent cooking solutions into the lakes or rivers. These organic materials decompose and in doing so rob the water of oxygen, thus seriously harming fish populations. Since lignosulphonates are strongly fluorescent, the flow of organic wastes into the rivers can be detected and mapped. Other industrial effluents such as detergents, for example, can be checked in the same way.

CHAPTER III

BEYOND THE VISIBLE

We will now pass from the sensors and systems used in the visible part of the spectrum to those used in the invisible part, namely, the infrared and microwave regions. Admittedly we have already mentioned the infrared in the last chapter, but this was only the near infrared from about 750 to 3000 nm (or, since we are now approaching the longer wavelength area, we will say from 0.75 to 3 μm). Waves in the near infrared range behave very much like optical waves; their properties are similar, and they are detected and recorded in much the same way. The near infrared range is generally recorded and becomes part of the spectral signature of an object. The information provided is particularly valuable in the fields of agriculture and forestry.

In the far infrared from 3.0 to 1000 μm the situation changes; the longer wavelengths allow other properties to be measured, and the means of detection are quite different. The waves are less likely to be absorbed and scattered in their passage through the atmosphere and are able to penetrate haze and fog.

We cannot take photographs in the thermal infrared region directly with an ordinary camera. For one thing it would be difficult to get suitable film and the camera itself would radiate some infrared energy which would fog the film. Just as we must make an ordinary camera lightproof, so we would have to make an infrared camera heatproof. This would entail cooling the whole camera and film to extremely low temperatures, a procedure which would not be practicable.

Therefore we go over once again to a scanning system similar to that used in the multispectral scanner just described. Historically, infrared scanning systems were in use before multispectral scanners since they were developed for the Armed Services. They are simpler in design and operation. An infrared scanner was not included as part of the instrumentation in Landsat, but several forms have been used in other satellites, and infrared sensing formed part of the sensor package in Skylab. It has been used extensively in airborne experiments.

There is a multitude of infrared scanning systems, varying in optical design, scanning arrangements and types of detectors used. As it would be tedious to describe them all, we will take a very simple one and look at it in some detail, knowing that all the others are merely modifications of this. A schematic diagram is shown in Figure 27.

Thermal radiation from the ground is picked up by a rotating mirror, whose face, about 10 cms in diameter, is 45° to its axis. During the rotation, the mirror sweeps across the terrain below it in a direction at right angles to the line of flight; an optical system focuses this energy on to a small detector. This is of a semi-conductive photo-voltaic cell type which converts radiation of varying intensity into a varying electric current, in much the same way as is done in the multispectral scanner. This varying current is then fed to a tape recorder and converted into some sort of visual display.

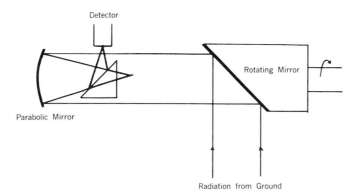

Figure 27. Schematic Diagram of a Thermal Infrared Scanner.

You will notice that with this arrangement no film is needed in the instrument itself; the process of photography is removed from the detection of thermal radiation. The only point at which we have to be particularly careful about extraneous radiation is at the detector itself. This detector head is very small, and so it is a relatively easy matter to shield it. It is usually mounted inside a protective case containing liquid nitrogen, which is so cold that practically no thermal radiation emanates from it. This arrangement has the effect of giving a larger signal-to-noise ratio, which, as we mentioned before, is one of the desirable attributes of sensors. In fact, most of these detectors will not operate above a certain critical temperature. How about resolution, another desirable attribute? In the case of aircraft this will depend on its height. At an altitude of 1000 metres the area of ground under the mirror from which radiation may be picked up will be a circle about 2.5 metres (8 ft.) in diameter; you can see therefore that it will be possible to discern quite small details. After processing, the images may be presented on a 5 inch black and white film. If we look at the negatives, the darkest parts will represent the highest temperatures, but we cannot know what the temperature is unless we calibrate the instrument in some way; this means we find the shade of grey which corresponds to a particular temperature and then we can compare all other shades of grey with it. This is done in the scanner itself. It is rotating, but it will be picking up radiation from the scene for only quite a small part of its time, about 1/4 of its cycle; for the other 3/4 it is virtually dead. It is in the dead part of its cycle that the sensor is calibrated by allowing the mirror to look in turn at two standard thermal sources set at different temperatures. In this way an absolute brightness temperature scale may be worked out for the whole range. We neglect here possible small errors due to absorption and self-emission in the atmosphere itself.

If we look at an image of an area as obtained by far infrared (as in Figure 16) we shall see a rather unfamiliar scene; it will be quite different from the one we see by visible light, and the interpretation will require some experience on the part of the interpreter. We shall know that the same shade of grey represents the same brightness temperature, but our eyes are unfortunately not very sensitive to shades of grey unless the areas are bordering on each other. It is extremely difficult to match a grey in one part of the picture with a grey in another part, if they are separated from each other. We are, however, able to differentiate very well indeed between different colours. By means of a technique known as *colour density slicing* it is possible to transform these shades of grey, or density, into different colours, so that one shade of grey may be changed into one colour, say red, and another shade may be changed into another colour, say yellow. It then becomes very easy to match brightness temperatures by matching colours.

An example of this may be seen in Plate I, which represents the temperature variations produced as the effluent from the nuclear power plant at Pickering, Ontario, flows into Lake Ontario; it covers a temperature range from 9.66°C to 17.00°C. Temperatures outside this range appear white. There are two areas of white in the picture, one above 17.00°C (at the immediate exit from the plant) and the other below 9.66°C (further out into the lake at the bottom). In the photograph the dark red represents a temperature range from 15.77°C. to 17.00°C; the lighter red from 14.55°C to 15.77°C; green 13.32°C to 14.55°C; mauve 12.10°C to 13.32°C; dark blue 10.88°C to 12.10°C; light blue 9.66°C to 10.88°C.

At the top right of the picture we can see the cool water (shades of blue between two narrow white containing walls) being taken into the plant from the lake. To the left is the effluent (white) flowing out at a temperature above 17°C. As it passes further out into the lake, the temperature falls and we can see the way in which mixing of the two waters takes place.

It is obvious that infrared scanning provides an excellent method of tracing the hot spots on the earth's surface, be they due to volcanic activity or forest fires. Just before a volcano erupts, such photographs have shown that certain thermal anomalies exist at the site, and so it might be possible to use thermal infrared techniques as part of a warning system. This would be particularly useful if we could record these images on a sequential basis from satellites.

One of the most practical applications in recent years has been the use of aerial infrared imagery (or aerial thermography as it is called) for the monitoring of heat loss from buildings and underground steam pipes. The need for energy conservation measures and the rapid escalation in the price of oil have made us all conscious of heat wastage and insulation efficiencies of our houses. The infrared scanner operating from an aircraft flying at 300 to 500 m above ground allows rapid and inexpensive surveys to be made of towns and industrial areas. Generally two photographs are taken – an infrared image at night and a daytime photograph, either in black and white or natural colour, to delineate the features of the scene in which we are interested. Figure 28(a) shows a daytime photograph of an industrial building, while (b) shows the corresponding nighttime thermogram. In the thermogram lighter shades represent the higher temperatures. A smoke stack, D, shows up very clearly and also a glass dome, E. Operating vents, F, show where the escaping hot air has warmed up the roof around them. Variations can be seen in the amount of heat escaping from the roof and they correspond to the type of construction of the roof. Part A represents a roof of conventional construction more than ten years old, while part C had been reroofed and reinsulated within the previous year. Part B is shown to be slightly warmer than the rest; the heat loss was found to be due to the fact that there was no insulation here except for a wooden ceiling. The lighter colour of the walls shows that more heat is lost through the walls than through the roof.

The value of such photographs for complete surveys of city buildings is self-evident. The methods were developed as part of the remote sensing programme of C.C.R.S. but have become so routine and so much in demand that all contracts for such surveys are now turned over to industrial companies. Many agencies, provincial authorities and utility companies have implemented schemes for carrying out studies so that homeowners can be made aware of inadequacies in their house insulation – a very practical end to what at one time must have seemed an ivory tower development.

Infrared techniques are also useful for detecting underground fires in abandoned coal mines and hot spots in shale heaps. It has been known in the past for workers to fall into holes in shale tips when fires were smouldering below the surface but were invisible from above. To be able to identify these positions from above would save many lives. These techniques may also be useful in helping to detect oil spills at sea and in delineating geothermal activity, hot springs, etc. In a world running short of power this might be a particularly important contribution to the

(a)

(b)

Figure 28. Application of IR Thermography to the
Heat Loss of Buildings.

(a) Photograph of an Industrial Building
(b) Nighttime Thermogram of the Same Building

world economy. One of the most important applications of infrared scanning is in the fighting of forest fires which will be dealt with in Chapter IX.

It stands to reason that infrared imagery can detect not only hot spots against a cooler background, but also cold spots against a warmer background. This has proved useful in locating potential frost pockets in terrain – a great boon to foresters and fruit growers. Again further details of this application will be given in Chapter IX.

Moving now into the microwave region gives a whole new dimension to the science of remote sensing. The great advantage of microwave radiation is that it can be used night and day in almost any kind of weather. Microwave techniques may be broken into two classes – passive and active. The first class of instruments is exemplified by radiometers, the second by radar imaging systems, scatterometers and altimeters.

In broad terms radiometers for all wavelengths work on the same principle. Radiation is gathered from a certain area, accepted by the instrument and recorded. In the case of the infrared radiometer already described, the radiation falls on a mirror and by means of an optical system is focussed on to a detector which converts the radiation to an electric current. In the case of a microwave radiometer the radiation is received by an antenna system, which passes the signals to a radio detector circuit, where it is again converted into a current and recorded.

As in the case of infrared techniques, microwaves are used to detect thermal radiation emitted by ground objects and to measure temperature. The temperature as recorded in the sensor is, of course, the temperature corresponding to the radiation it receives and is again referred to as *Brightness* temperature; this will be related to the ground temperature but will not be quite the same, partly because of ground emissivity and partly because rays sent up through the atmosphere will undergo certain changes in their journey from ground to sensor. The correlation between actual ground temperature and the intensity of signals as received by the sensor is not as good as when using infrared systems.

We saw that the amount of thermal radiation emitted by an object depends on its emissivity and on its temperature. In the microwave region the emissivity of various materials differs quite widely from one material to another, which means that the amount of radiation sent out by different objects at the same temperature may differ considerably. Also the dependence of intensity of radiation on temperature for any single object is not as marked as it is at shorter wavelengths. It is not therefore a very good way of measuring variations in temperature, but it is an excellent way of measuring differences in emissivities, and therefore it is an excellent technique for detecting boundaries between different materials with different emissivities. For example, ice has an emissivity at these wavelengths more than twice that of water. Therefore, if ice and water are at the same temperature, ice will radiate twice as much energy into the microwave sensor as will water. If we have a water surface, such as the sea, with ice floes in it, the water will appear to be colder than the ice. If signals from such a scene are converted to photographic type imagery, we will see light-coloured ice floating in a dark sea. The implications for the study of ice conditions in the Arctic are obvious, and microwave methods have yielded some very promising results. The whole of the polar ice cap has been mapped with extraordinary success as Plate II will demonstrate. This was obtained by the satellite Nimbus-5 at a wavelength of 1.55 cm (19.35 Ghz).

To those of us who are not experts in interpretation such a picture looks interesting but confusing. The first thing to remember is that the colour code of temperatures shown below does not indicate absolute temperatures but "brightness" temperatures. Since ice has a much higher "brightness" temperature than water at the same temperature, we see the boundary between ice and water as dark blue, whereas ice areas of the same temperature are light blue. The Arctic Ocean is a dynamic system and this ice-water edge is continually changing; we can even have open water at the North Pole on occasion. Such pictures observed at regular intervals of time allow the experts to study the changing conditions. it is also of interest to know something about the age of ice. First-year ice looks very different from multiyear ice because the degree to which it is packed affects its emission characteristics. The average "brightness" temperature of multiyear ice is about 220°K, while that for first-year ice is about 250°K. On such a picture multiyear ice will appear blue, while first-year ice will appear yellow or green. We can see areas of first-year ice in Baffin Bay just to the west of Greenland, whereas much of the ice further north is multiyear ice. Since multiyear ice is less easily dispersed and very resistant to icebreakers, such information is important. An actual application of detection of ice of different ages is discussed in Chapter VIII and illustrated in Figure 60.

As an example of a microwave radiometer, we will look at the one originally designed for Nimbus G Spacecraft and later put aboard Seasat. This was called a Scanning Multifrequency Microwave Radiometer (SMMR). It is capable of taking measurements of the horizontally and vertically polarized components over five frequency bands, namely centred at 6.6, 10.69, 18.0, 21.0 and 37.0 GHz (i.e. with corresponding wavelengths of 4.55, 2.81, 1.67, 1.43 and 0.81 cm.). Why so many frequency bands? As already mentioned the strength of the signal received depends on the temperature of the object and its emission characteristics. The emission characteristics, in turn, depend on the emissivity of the material, the surface conditions (i.e. the roughness or smoothness) and the wavelength of the radiation being measured. The magnitude of the accepted signal also depends on the absorption and scattering in the atmosphere, again dependent on wavelength. With so many factors involved it might seem at first sight difficult to sort out all these variables to interpret the final values. By taking measurements at several different wavelengths a mathematician is able to do this. When flown in Seasat at a height of about 800 km the instrument scanned a swath of earth 595 km wide at an angle of 49°; an instantaneous record was given from an area varying from 87 x 144 km to 16 x 25 km depending on the frequency (6.6 to 37.0 GHz). It was thus able to create an image of the radiation from the earth and to measure, for example, the absolute sea temperature to an accuracy of $2^{\circ}K$, or the relative temperature to $1^{\circ}K$ and the ocean surface wind speeds of 0 - 50 m/sec to an accuracy of $\pm$ 2 m/sec.

The radiation emanating from the earth is modified by several factors other than the actual temperature. As already mentioned, it will be affected by the roughness of the surface. There will also be a small reflected component of radiation from the sun and from space, and there may be some radiation from clouds and atmospheric gases. These will add to the sum total of radiation measured. Against this must be set the fact that some radiation is absorbed in its path through the atmosphere, particularly at the shorter wavelengths. Scientists have designed equations which will allow compensation to be made for these effects at different wavelengths. We can put these seemingly annoying factors to good use in studying the atmosphere itself. By taking measurements at several frequencies and two different states of polarization, we can obtain data for putting into equations, and radiometers may thus be used to probe the atmosphere. For example, by measuring the emission at frequencies close to 22.3 GHz, we can get information on the water vapour of the atmosphere and can obtain a water vapour profile of a column of atmosphere between the ground and the spacecraft. In the same way we can obtain an oxygen profile.

In the spacecraft the incoming radiation is collected by a hornshaped antenna which scans the path to acquire an analogue record. It is then converted in the instrument to give a digital signal and telemetered to earth for final processing. The resolution may seem disappointingly low, being of the order of kilometres, but this is the price that has to be paid for the longer wavelengths and its associated advantage of all-weather capability. The research associated with this radiometer represents an important step in the development of an instrument for the Space Shuttle Programme. Since this satellite will be large enough to carry a larger antenna the resolution should be improved.

In the meantime, we are getting some valuable data. The application to sea-ice has already been demonstrated. The data gathered can be put together to provide information not only on sea surface temperatures but also on foam and roughness, on types of ice, on wind speeds, on water content of soils and, in fact, on different types of soil and rock, on snow formation, etc.

We will now turn our attention to active microwave systems. Radiation is sent out from the aircraft or spacecraft, sometimes as a continuous beam, sometimes in short pulses, and the characteristics of the reflected beam are recorded. This is the basic principle of radar. Radar is an acronym for Radio Detection and Ranging. It owes much of its development to the events of the Second World War. In the early 1930's experiments were carried out in which a pulse of radio waves was sent out from a transmitter and then, after reflection from an object, was received back again by a radio receiver alongside it. We know the speed of the waves since all electromagnetic radiation travels in space at the same speed of 300,000 km/sec or 186,000 miles/sec. Therefore by measuring the time for the pulse to travel to the object and back again, we can calculate the distance. From these simple beginnings the technology of radar developed apace. During the War it advanced so that it could be used not only for detection and ranging but also for direction finding; it was used to direct searchlights, to control anti-aircraft gun fire, to locate submarines and to navigate ships. After the War radar was put to more peaceful purposes. First of all we had the development of radio telescopes for studying the heavens, radar methods for the detection of storms and weather forecasting, for air traffic control, and for the avoidance of collisions between ships at sea. Since radar pulses can be used for ranging, it is not surprising to find that they can be used for altimeters in airplanes. The time for a pulse to travel from plane to ground and back tells us the height of the plane and, if the plane is travelling at a constant height over hilly ground, it tells us something about the topography of the land below.

The equipment itself consists essentially of a transmitter capable of producing waves of the required wavelength and of sending them out in pulses, an antenna so aligned as to be able to send out and receive the energy in the direction desired, a receiver for detecting the return signals, and some means of recording or displaying the data received. These are the essential elements. In general there are two basic types of equipment which utilize these principles. In one of them the antenna rotates and so scans the whole field of view, and the signals are presented on a circular screen in a cathode ray tube. This type of Plan Position Indicator (PPI) is one of several that were developed during World War II and it is now widely used by the armed services and by navigators of aircraft and ships. It is good for ranging over modest distances, but its resolution is not very good.

With radio waves, resolution is dependent on the ratio of antenna length to wavelength, or, in the case of the dish type of antenna system you see around the country in many radar installations, on the ratio of dish diameter to wavelength. To achieve a high resolution, therefore, we want to use a long antenna or a short wavelength. There are limits to the shortness of the wavelength because, as we have been, we run into problems of atmospheric interference. There are also mechanical limits to the length of an antenna if it is rotating.

To overcome these difficulties a system was devised called SLAR, an acronym for Side-Looking Airborne Radar. Here the antennas do not rotate but are fixed along the length of the plane, one on each side. As the name of the system implies, they are looking out sideways at the surrounding countryside, and they may be nearly as long as the plane itself.

An aircraft carrying a typical SLAR system will have two long antennas, probably about 4 or 5 metres long (i.e. about 12 or 15 feet), fitted one each side of the plane. A high-powered transmitter within the aircraft sends short, rapid pulses of radio waves alternately to each of these antennas, which in turn radiates them to earth. They are partially reflected back again into the receiver and are recorded on a tape, or used to modulate a cathode ray tube to form a photographic-type image as in the case of other sensors. As we can see in Figure 29, the waves are radiated sideways and below the plane so as to form a narrow fan-shaped beam which illuminates the ground below. As the plane moves forward, a swath of terrain is swept out on each side of the aircraft and the signals being returned from this swath are recorded. The length of track running in the direction of flight is, in effect, scanned from side to side, and so a picture may be built up strip by strip as in the case of the infrared system.

The return signal from the edge of the swath nearest to the plane will arrive back first and step-by-step the track will be rapidly traversed. Scanning across the track is achieved without the need for a mechanical scanning system. The flight of the aircraft will then carry the instrument on to the next strip and the process will be repeated. We can see that the interval between pulses must

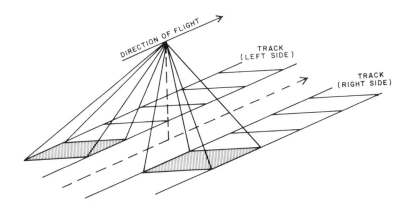

Figure 29. Aircraft fitted with SLAR System.

be of such duration that there are no gaps in the film. The
interval will be determined by a number of factors including
wavelength, resolution required, velocity and height of
aircraft and by antenna geometry. Since the same antenna
is both transmitting and receiving signals, special circuits
have to be designed which will block the transmitter while a
signal is being received, and block the receiver while the
pulse is being radiated. The result of all this will be an
image where strong signals give a bright spot and weaker
signals will give varying shades of grey.

The pictures which result from radar techniques require
a fair amount of experience in their interpretation. The
fact that at first sight they appear somewhat similar to
those we are familiar with in light photography presents
some pitfalls because there are many differences in the way
they are produced. In both cases the strength of the signal
depends on reflectivity, or back-scatter of the incident
radiation; but, with optical photography the amount of light

reflected from an object is determined mainly by the absorptivity of the material of which it is made, and as we have seen selective absorption gives rise to colours, while with radar images the amount of radiation reflected is determined mainly by the dielectric constant and surface roughness of the material. Materials like metal, for example, reflect very strongly. This is the reason why power lines and small metallic objects, which are well below the theoretical resolution of the system, may still be distinguishable.

We discussed the effects of surface and the phenomenon of specular and diffuse reflection in Chapter I. Whether a surface behaves like a mirror and reflects specularly, or whether it reflects diffusely depends on the smoothness or granularity of its surface and the relation of the size of the irregularities to the wavelength of the radiation impinging on it. A surface which may be a diffuse reflector to visible light may be a specular reflector to the longer wavelengths of microwave radiation. A specular reflection will give a very intense signal if we are recording in the direction of its return, but it will only give a very weak signal in all other directions. In radar where the "illumination" falls on the ground at an angle to the vertical, the radiation will therefore bounce away in the opposite direction and will be lost; this will result in a dark spot on the image. Water, concrete and roads are specular reflectors at microwave wavelengths so that if horizontal they appear black on a radar image. On the other hand, as already mentioned, corner reflectors, formed by buildings standing at right angles to the roads on which they are built, will send the radiation right back to the source; since in a radar system the transmitter and the receiver are in the same place, we will see a very intense bright spot on the image. A city which has a number of large blocks of buildings will show a speckled effect due to these corner reflectors. Fields of vegetation will show diffuse reflection and will give a mottled effect of shades of grey; small waves on water and ridges on ice also act as diffuse reflectors. For this reason radar is a good system for studying some textures.

In addition, there will of course be shadows from larger irregularities in the terrain. In the case of radar images from aircraft, the angle may be low and long shadows will result; also the shadows will be more elongated the further they are from the aircraft. Immediately below, the shadows will be short; as the range increases the angle will become smaller and the shadows longer. The effect of sloping surfaces in the terrain also leads to complications. If the radar beam falls on a slope away from the plane, the reflected ray will be returned away from it giving a very weak signal; if the radiation falls on a surface sloping towards the plane, it will be reflected back again and will give a very strong signal as Figure 30 shows.

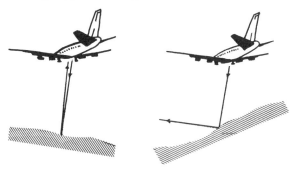

Figure 30. Effect of Terrain on Return of Radar Signal.

What about the resolution of such a system? It will differ in the two directions along track and across track; these are generally referred to as azimuthal resolution and range resolution respectively.

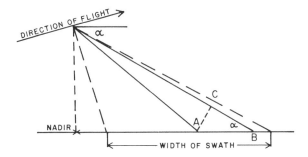

Figure 31. Cross-Track Resolution of a SLAR System.

Let us consider cross-track or range resolution first. This determines the degree to which we can distinguish between objects as we move out from the near edge of the swath in a sideways direction. The cross-track resolution is therefore determined by the accuracy with which we can measure range differences and this is dependent on the duration of the pulse sent out. A shorter pulse will give rise to a higher resolution.

Suppose two points A and B located within the same swath in Figure 31 are just resolvable; A being nearer will send back a signal first, while a signal from B will be returned later. The time elapsing between the reception of the signal from A and its reception from B will be caused by the extra distance the beam has to travel (i.e. twice the distance CB). This distance must be traversed in a time greater than the length of time of the pulse, or in other words the pulse length, otherwise the two points could not be differentiated. The distance on the ground, AB, will be CB/cos , where is the depression angle. It is therefore easy to see that if the pulse length is made shorter the distance AB will be less and so the resolution improved. It is generally reckoned that two objects can be distinguished from each other if their slant ranges differ by at least half the distance traversed by the pulse in its duration. Range resolution is therefore entirely dependent on pulse length and not at all on slant range. The distance on the ground corresponding to this slant range will depend on the angle of depression of the beam or the height of the plane.

We have said that to get better resolution we could shorten the pulse, but the fundamental lower limit is governed by band width. A shorter pulse would mean less energy transmitted, and the return signal would be weakened. To overcome this problem, a new technique has been developed, called *chirp*, which enables a long pulse with an adequate amount of energy to be, in effect, compressed into a very intense, short pulse. This has enabled range resolutions of better than 3 metres.

How about azimuthal resolution? As the plane travels along its path, it gathers information strip by strip across the track. The resolution in the fore-and aft-direction will depend on the width of these strips. If two objects, C and D, are both situated within the same strip they will both be

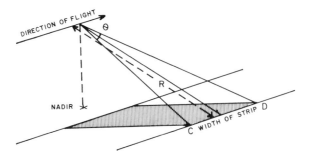

Figure 32. Azimuthal Resolution of a SLAR System.

imaged together, and it will be impossible to distinguish the one from the other. A narrow beam will give a high resolution and *vice versa*. Since the beam is fan-shaped, the width of the strip will depend on the distance from the plane. Immediately below the plane the strip will be much narrower than it would be a long way out. For this reason, instead of specifying the azimuthal resolution as metres on the ground, it is generally described by the angular width of the beam. This is expressed as milliradians, or thousandths of a radian, and is denoted by θ as in Figure 32. From this it is very easy to get the ground resolution for any range because if R is the range of an object from the aircraft and is the angle expressed in radians, then, by definition of the radian, the ground resolution, S, is given by

$$S = R\theta$$

This resolution may also be expressed in its relationship to the wavelength (λ) and length of the antenna (L) as

$$S = \frac{R\lambda}{L}$$

Supposing a system has a resolution of 8 milliradians. At a range of 10,000 feet the resolution on the ground would be something a little less than 80 feet. At 100,000 feet it would be a little less than 800 feet, and so on. This is poor resolution. For ice reconnaisance, where the icefloes are

large and not too much detail is required, this resolution
may be adequate; at normal flying altitudes it would be
about 30 to 100 m. But, if we take the same radar and put
it in a satellite, the resolution would be very poor. Seasat,
orbiting at a height of some 700 km would produce a beam
width on the ground of 22 km and that would be quite
useless. How do we improve the situation?

We want somehow to make this beam narrower in the
direction of flight. We know the beam width is determined
partly by the length of the antennas or by the aperture. We
want to increase the size of the aperture, but we cannot
make the antennas much longer or they would become
mechanically unstable. A new system was therefore
devised, in which a so-called *synthetic aperture* is used, as
opposed to the *real aperture* which has just been described.
This is a rather complex operation. The method involves
taking measurements of the signals reflected from any one
point at the ground from several positions of the aircraft as
it travels over it; in other words, it is taking measurements
at different angles. Imagine for the sake of simplicity a
series of just 5 points on the ground with an aircraft passing
over them from left to right as shown in Figure 33.

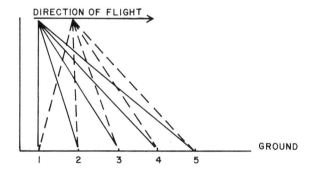

Figure 33. Return of Signals from Synthetic Aperture Radar.

The radar antenna will emit a pulsed signal of frequency, f. When it is immediately over 1, the antenna will receive a return signal of the same frequency or wavelength as it sent out. This will be taped and sent to a computer which will store it away in its memory. It will also receive a return signal from 2, 3, 4 and 5, in that order of time. Since the aircraft will be moving, there will be a Doppler shift of frequency as described in Chapter I; from these points therefore the frequency will be greater (i.e. the wavelength will be less). These signals also are stored away in the computer's memory. The aircraft will then move over point 2 and the process will be repeated. It will receive a return signal from 2 of the same frequency and signals from 3, 4 and 5 of higher frequency. It will also look back at point 1, and in this case the frequency will be decreased since the aircraft is moving away from that point. The data on each of these points will be passed to the memory of the computer. When the aircraft is over 2 and it receives the data from 1, the computer may say to itself "I remember that point on the ground; I received a bit of information on it a moment ago; now I have another bit from another angle. I will put these together in an appropriate form to see just how bright that point was." So that is how the computer works. it collects data for each point along the track as the aircraft views it from different angles and it does this for many hundreds of points. It also goes through the same process for every point across the swath. We are beginning to get some idea of the complexity of the process of unscrambling the signals we receive to give a picture. The arrangement has the effect of synthetically increasing the length of the antenna and so increasing the resolution. A further advantage is that whereas the resolution of the real aperture SLAR is dependent on the range of a point from the aircraft, the resolution of the synthetic aperture SLAR is almost independent of range. Synthetic aperture systems can therefore get above the bad weather, where the plane is more stable; this again aids in giving good pictures. Systems now being used in aircraft are obtaining resolutions of something better than 3 metres (9 feet) in both range and azimuth directions. It does not matter as far as detail is concerned if we are flying some metres above the earth in an aircraft or hundreds of kilometres above the earth in a satellite. Another surprising result is that it can be shown mathematically that the azimuthal resolution is given by

$$S = \frac{L}{2}$$

so that the smaller we make the length of the antenna, L, the better is the resolution - the exact opposite of the situation we had before.

Anyone familiar with optics will recognize synthetic aperture techniques as being akin to interferometry. The tapes recording these return signals are, in fact, referred to as interferograms. Mathematical techniques are used to interpret this data in order to create an image.

Readers may not like this somewhat primitive explanation of synthetic aperture radar. For anyone wanting a slightly more sophisticated approach which is not too mathematical, an excellent treatment is given in an article titled "Side-looking Airborne Radar" by Homer Jensen, L.C. Graham, Leonard Porcello and Emmett N. Leith in Scientific American, October, 1977. This should be available in most public libraries.

As we see, active microwave systems from space would not be able to provide imagery of any value without the use of synthetic aperture techniques. At present we can achieve a resolution of better than 6 m. in the along track direction, which is extraordinarily good and far surpasses the resolution of multispectral scanners in satellites. Unfortunately we are not able to make full use of this theoretical resolution because of a phenomenon known as *speckle*, which is associated with the monochromatic and coherent nature of the radiation. Let us consider lasers for a moment because, as we saw earlier, lasers also are a souce of monochromatic and coherent radiation.

When ordinary light is reflected from an object such as a flat wall, the spot appears uniformly bright. The reason for this is that the light shone on it is incoherent; although each individual train of waves will change phase on reflection, it will make no difference to the overall brightness because we are looking at an average overall effect. When light from a laser is shone on to the same wall, the trains of waves on reflection will be out-of-phase. The wall is not perfectly flat and has a roughness consisting of peaks and valleys which may only be of the order of the wavelength of light. Therefore some waves will have to travel on to the surface and off again a slightly different distance and the regularity of the waveforms will be upset. However, since they are nevertheless of the same wavelength, they will interfere with each other in a regular manner; sometimes the amplitudes will be added together and at another spot they will partly cancel each other out. This gives rise to intensely bright specks mixed up with darker specks, and the whole surface appears minutely speckled. The speckles remain steady as long as the laser, the surface and the viewer remain absolutely steady. Since this seldom happens, the spot of light takes on a scintillating, shimmering appearance. The same thing happens when a radar beam is reflected except that you cannot see it until after the image has been processed. To improve the condition a system of computing has been devised which will average out these speckles. Normally one would take all the returns for any given point on the ground and add them together in a coherent fashion. Considering the radar system on Seasat, this would give a resolution of 6 m. on the ground, but the image would be speckled. There would be a great variation in intensity over an area which is, in fact, reflecting quite uniformly. Now, if instead of processing the full aperture coherently the returns are broken up into chunks and these chunks added together incoherently, this speckle would be reduced. In doing so the resolution would unfortunately also be reduced, but this is a compromise we have to make. If we look at the inscription on a radar image we may see a cryptic statement – "4 looks". This means that the total number of returns has been broken up into 4 chunks; the resolution would be reduced to 24 m in the azimuth direction – a convenient figure because the resolution in the range direction is 25 m and so it would be approximately the same in all directions. The greater number of looks the poorer is the resolution. 4 looks would not produce as good an image as a photograph; this would probably require about 100 looks but too much resolution would be lost. At 4 looks the resolution is generally adequate as the radar image in Figure 52 shows. Further details on processing the radar signals to create imagery are given in Chapter V.

In designing a radar system for looking at earth features there are many factors to consider. What is the best wavelength to use? What is the best angle of viewing? How about the state of polarization? and so on. As always the best condition for one purpose may not be the best for another. The best conditions for collecting data on sea ice may not be the best for land areas, and so we have to compromise.

First of all let us consider wavelength. Chapter I tables the wavelength bands and their associated letters. The lower limit is set by the fact that at wavelengths below about 1 cm., strong reflections are received from clouds and raindrops. In designing a radar for meteorological purposes we would therefore choose the shorter wavelengths. For imagery of the earth we would use longer wavelengths so that we could use radar in all weather conditions. In general as the wavelength is increased penetration is increased. The two bands most commonly used are X-band (2.4 to 3.8 cm) and L-band (15.0 to 30 cm). The radar system on board the C.C.R.S. Convair aircraft has both wavebands. X-band gives a better ice picture since waves at this wavelength are more strongly reflected by ice boundaries, and the resolution is good. L-band provides greater penetration and so waves of this wavelength tend to give less detail. However if we put radar in a satellite, there are certain technical difficulties with regard to weight and power supplies for X-band which make the L-band easier to handle. Seasat L-band radar operated at a wavelength of 23.5 cm. There are certain advantages in going over to an intermediate band - the C-band (3.8 to 7.5 cm), where the technical difficulties are simpler to cope with than those associated with X-band, and the application for ice studies are more suitable than L-band.

With regard to the state of polarization of waves being sent out and received, the two systems (on the aircraft and on the satellite) are able to transmit and receive back horizontally polarized radiation (HH - horizontal transmit and horizontal receive). The aircraft radar is also able to transmit vertically polarized radiation; on reflection the state of polarization may be changed according to the nature of the ground object with which it interacts, and the aircraft will receive back only that part of the radiation which is horizontally polarized. The system is then said to be a VH system (vertical transmit and horizontal receive). We would then be looking at the energy which was *cross-polarized* and this gives a picture which can be quite different from the *like-polarized* HH system mentioned above. It gives a different kind of information; for example, power poles, telephone poles and other vertical objects give very strong vertically polarized return signals which allow them to be detected although they are normally beyond the resolution of the system. The agriculturists have found some interesting differences between vertically and horizontally polarized returns when looking at imagery of trees and other vegetation. More will be said on the subject of polarization when we discuss an instrument called the scatterometer.

The SAR system on the Convair has four receiving channels, X-band, HH and VH and L-band, HH and VH. The aircraft is thus an excellent tool for experimental use and a number of investigations are being carried out which will enable us to learn more about the best parameters to use for radar imagery under different circumstances. An interesting image may be seen in Figure 52 which will be discussed later in Chapter VII. An experimental X and C band synthetic aperture radar is now under development and will be installed shortly. The C band was chosen partly as a result of C band scatterometer studies in connection with agriculture and soil moisture problems. It will be particularly valuable as a means of getting experience in this area which may be used in the proposed Canadian RADARSAT programme and also in the French satellite SPOT, in the European Space Agency ERS-1 satellite and in the proposed Canadian and Japanese programmes.

One more factor which we should consider at this point is the angle at which the beam from the aircraft or satellite strikes the ground. As shown in Figure 34 below, we refer to the angle the beam makes with the vertical direction as the *incident angle* or the *angle of incidence* (θ). The angle the beam makes with the horizontal is called the *depression angle* (α). We know that with ordinary light it sometimes makes quite a difference if we look at something at a high angle of incidence, where the light is grazing the surface, or if we look straight down at it. The grazing angles will allow us to see more small surface detail, but if we are looking at deep valleys and tall hills a grazing angle would only obscure the view. The same thing happens with radar; for small details a higher angle of incidence is helpful in providing a shadow effect, whereas in mountainous areas a smaller angle would be required. We will include further discussion of angle of incidence together with questions of polarization after looking at the scatterometer.

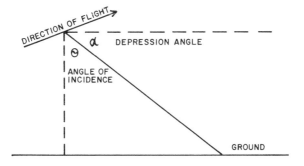

Figure 34. Angles of Incidence and Depression.

The scatterometer is also an active microwave instrument, but it does not provide imagery as does the radar system we have just being describing. Instead it acts as a profiler of terrain by plotting the intensity of a returned signal against position along a narrow path parallel to the aircraft or satellite track. When used over the ocean it can measure surface roughness and so, indirectly, the speed and direction of the wind. It has also proved valuable in ice studies.

The scatterometer may transmit a pulsed signal or a continuous beam of energy and it sends this out in a very narrow fan-shaped beam. The transmitted beam has an angular width of only 2º in the direction at right angles to the plane's flight, but about 120º along the track direction – 60 º fore and 60º aft. The signal received back from the ground will differ in frequency from that sent out because of the Doppler effect mentioned above. In the forward direction the frequency would be increased; in the backward direction the frequency would be decreased. Since the actual frequency depends on the relative speed between the object and the moving plane, it is easy to see that from the frequency which we measure we can obtain the position of the return signal; knowing the altitude of the plane we can calculate the angle of incidence of the beam. From this data we can construct a curve in which the strength of the signal is plotted against incident angle, or against distance from the nadir. As the plane moves along a flight path, a profiling curve is given showing contours of variations of signal strength along the ground (or sea, when used over the ocean).

The signal is generally referred to as the back-scatter cross-section; i.e. it is the total amount of back-scattered or reflected radiation per square metre. In a satellite which remains in orbit a fixed distance from the ground, the "foot-print" of the beam on the ground is constant, and so the total reflected energy is all we need to measure. In an aircraft the "foot-print" will be larger for higher altitudes and the signal less. We therefore need to relate signal strength to altitude in order to make it a measure of the ground characteristics.

The scatterometer we are considering (i.e. as fitted to the Convair-580 at C.C.R.S.) is able to transmit signals which are either horizontally polarized or vertically polarized. It can receive either of these after reflection as horizontally or vertically polarized waves. We can therefore have horizontally polarized transmission and horizontally polarized return (HH), like-polarization, or horizontally polarized transmission and vertically polarized return (HV), cross-polarization. In the same way we can have (VV) and (VH) systems. Our experience with the various angles of incidence and states of polarization is not very great at the moment, but a considerable amount of research is at present being carried out in this area and the results are very promising and extraordinarily interesting.

"Well", you may say, "that is all very well, but what good are they to anybody?"

To begin with, it is not difficult to see that the scatterometer with its flexibility as regards angle of incidence and state of polarization is an ideal research tool for finding out the best design features for a satellite. There are indications that the best conditions were not those used in Seasat. The final words on the subject have not yet been uttered, but it may be interesting at this stage for us to look at an experiment recently carried out by a group of scientists from the Canada Centre of Remote Sensing, Intera Environmental Consultants Ltd. of Ottawa and the Environmental Research Institute of Michigan. The detection and tracking of icebergs is of prime importance in the operation of large supply ships or tankers in the Eastern Arctic, and for the safe and efficient operation of off-shore drilling rigs in Lancaster Sound, Baffin Island and off the Labrador Coast. Using a scatterometer the experimenters sought to establish the best conditions for detecting bergs, bergy bits and old sea floes using different states of polarization of the beam and different angles of incidence. Reflections from a choppy sea produce a certain amount of clutter as a background to the signal, and this reduces the ability to detect some of the bergs. In order to evaluate the results, the measurements were therefore converted to signal-to-clutter ratios expressed as db's (a unit familiar to most engineers). As an example Figure 35 shows the scatterometer output (using VV conditions of polarization) plotted against time (from which, knowing the speed of the aircraft, we can calculate the position). This was done for different angles of incidence aft of the plane. It is interesting that at the higher angles of incidence the signal from the berg is higher than from the surrounding sea, but at lower angles of incidence it is lower. At some point in between the berg would not be detectable at all. Similar results were obtained for HH conditions of polarization. Results on ships also showed that the signal-to-clutter ratios can be quite low for small angles of incidence, despite the fact that ships are much better reflectors of microwaves than are icebergs.

Another thing to notice is that the strongest signals come from low angles of incidence, when the instrument is looking almost straight down on to the target. At higher angles, when the incident beam is more nearly approaching the horizontal, some of the energy will bounce away in the opposite direction and will be lost. It appears that there is a minimum angle of incidence if we wish to detect small ships

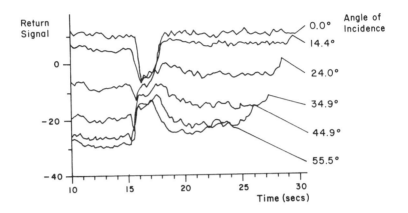

Courtesy of Canada Centre for Remote Sensing

Figure 35. Scatterometer Output from Iceberg as a Function of Time for Different (aft) Angles of Incidence.

in high seas; this will apply whether the microwave beam emanates from a radar or from a scatterometer. This may explain the fact that the synthetic aperture radar of Seasat, which operated at an incidence angle of 20°, did not do a good job of detecting icebergs or small ships in regions off the East Coast of Canada. it might be better in future satellites to increase the angle of incidence to about 45°. However, we cannot yet speak categorically on this point because the cross-over point at which there is minimum detectability could be at different angles for different frequencies.

The results also indicated that the best mode of polarization would be the HH condition in order to reduce sea clutter. Actually better results were given with cross-polarized than with like-polarized radiation, but the technical complexity of the system would deter its use in a satellite unless the results could be shown to be considerably improved.

Another series of experiments carried out in the Arctic concerned the classification of ice types. This was the result of a concerted effort by scientists from the Canada

Centre of Remote Sensing, the Department of Fisheries and the Environment and the U.S. Geological Survey. Using again a scatterometer, they sought to establish the optimum design features for an airborne imaging radar operating at a wavelength of 2 to 3 cm to be used as part of an ice reconnaissance sensor package. Again they paid particular attention to incident angle and polarization and they came to the conclusion that it would be best to avoid very large angles of incidence (greater than approximately 80º), and that cross-polarization conditions would give better differentiation between different ice-types but at the expense of higher cost and higher complexity. Since that time (1975), extremely promising results have been obtained in ice classifications despite the complexity of the phenomenon of reflection of microwaves from ice. Old ice, for example, has a high backscatter cross-section. This is due to the actual crystal structure and airpockets in the top 2 cm of ice. When looking at sea ice we are looking really at three materials - solid ice, liquid water and pockets of air and water vapour. These all have different dielectric constants and sea ice has different microwave signatures under different temperature conditions. However, by collecting together scatterometer and radiometer data under different conditions of look angle, polarization, etc., it has been shown that an improved differentiation of the major ice types can be achieved on the basis of their microwave signatures. However, the scatterometer and radiometer signatures change substantially under summer melting conditions, and it is no longer possible to identify different ice types as readily as under the colder conditions of the winter. Even under melting conditions the high resolution synthetic aperture radar imagery allows us to identify ice/water boundaries and old ice - a hazard to shipping and off-shore exploration.

With the further work which is proceeding at present, it should be possible to get even better information out of such systems, especially if we can afford to design specialized equipment for operating on a specific job, such as ice reconnaissance. Considering the importance of such knowledge for Canada in the management of her northern resources, this news is very encouraging.

CHAPTER IV

PLATFORMS

We now have a very sophisticated selection of sensors for different uses. How can we deploy these to make the best use of them for remote sensing purposes? What sort of platforms shall we mount them on?

We all know that the higher we go the further we can see. When man first started to study his environment, he did so, of necessity, from the ground. In order to see further he climbed a tree or better still a hill or a mountain. Then he built towers to enable him to spot forest fires and he used other sensors, binoculars and telescopes, to supplement his eyesight. When the first balloons were made, he seized the opportunity to leave his planet and look down on it from above, using cameras to record the scenes he saw. In time these balloons were succeeded by heavier-than-air machines, such as airplanes, helicopters, and rockets, and now by satellites and other spacecraft. A comprehensive study of our environment will make use of all these platforms, each making its own contribution in its own way. As we go higher, the scale will be smaller and we are, of course, not able to see so much detail. Thus detail must be sacrificed for a much better overall view in which whole geological structures can be seen at one time. Satellites enable world-wide coverage to be obtained within a very short period of time — something which was not possible before.

Let us take a look at some of these platforms and see what their particular advantages are.

Starting at ground level we have for a long time been using buoys, towers, etc., to which we affix our instruments for the measurement and collection of data. The weather forecasting scientists have made use of these for collecting data on temperature, rainfall, windspeeds, and other pertinent factors. Those who manage our water resources make use of earth-based or ocean-based platforms for assessing the quality of water, its temperature, rate of flow, turbidity, etc., and for recording water levels. These are not truly remote-sensing devices because, generally, the sensors are right there in contact with what they are measuring, but they are mentioned here because, with the advent of satellites, a new method has been presented for the handling of the data they provide. In the past the collection and dissemination of the data have posed problems because instruments were frequently located in places difficult to reach. There was generally no power available except for batteries, which had a limited life. Recent developments in the design of ocean-moored platforms, including batteries with much longer lives, have made a network system of floating buoys a more attractive proposition.

Many ways of retrieving the data from earth stations have also been developed, and one of the most interesting is the use of satellites or other spacecraft. Each data collection platform may carry a number of individual sensors. They may be selected to measure whatever we want, such as properties relating to the soil, oceans, lakes, and air, at selected places all over the globe. A transmitter mounted on the earth platform can radio this information to a data collection system in the satellite, which in turn can transmit it to some other place on earth. We shall be referring to this again when describing Landsat.

Historically the next stage in platform sophistication came with the use of balloons, and photographs were taken from some of the early balloons in the middle of the last century. There are several advantages to this method. A balloon can hover over an area for as long as is needed; it may be free-floating or it may be tethered; there is no vibration and little movement, an advantage as far as photography is concerned. It does not have to be blasted off the earth by an expensive launch vehicle; not only is it less expensive to put into operation, but there is less risk of damage to the instruments it carries; at the end of its mission it settles back on earth again quite gently, again reducing the danger of instrument damage. Alternatively the gondola in which the instruments are carried may be recovered by parachute. A very important consideration is that balloons are relatively cheap to produce and operate.

Although balloons provided one of the earliest ways of

lifting both men and instruments off the ground, they are by no means outdated, and modern developments have brought them to the fore again today. It is now possible for them to operate at heights of about 50 km. (over 160,000 feet) for fairly long periods of time with payloads of 1,800 kg. These altitudes are higher than can normally be attained with aircraft, and so balloons offer many advantages as platforms for testing sensors, under near-space conditions, before installing them irretrievably in satellites.

High altitude balloons are the nearest thing to spacecraft and, in fact, have some advantages over satellites. Their path is more flexible. As we shall see presently, in order for a satellite to be held stationary with respect to the earth (or to maintain it in a geostationary orbit, as the experts say) it has to be placed at a very high altitude of about 37,000 km (23,000 miles). At this height it is difficult to see any of the earth's detail. A balloon on the other hand can be kept more or less stationary at much lower heights for a considerable period of time. In order to hold the balloon steady at a predetermined position in the sky, two methods are possible. One is to tether it by cables, and the other is to provide it with power. With very low altitude operation tethering presents few problems, but for high altitude work it would be out of the question.

Helicopters offer some advantages as a platform from which photographs may be taken. They can hover over an area and can execute more complicated flight paths than aircraft (such as following roads or rivers), and they can also operate at lower altitudes. They are, however, subject to vibration, but this can be taken care of to some extent by anti-vibration mounts for the cameras, as of course must also be used in aircraft. They are relatively cheap to operate, flexible in planning and the information they provide is easily recoverable. They have been used successfully by foresters for assessing the volume of wood in the forests, by agriculturists for examining large areas of crops, and by surveyors in urban or mining areas.

At the present time aircraft are one of the most useful and most generally used platforms for remote-sensing systems. They can carry almost any kind of sensor – conventional photographic cameras, television cameras, multispectral scanners, infrared scanners, radar and other microwave devices, fluorosensors and so on. Since the information they acquire is easily recoverable, and since the instruments may be easily adapted and maintained, aircraft are very useful for trying out experimental ideas at a presatellite stage. A variety of different planes are used, the choice depending on the altitude at which they are to be flown, the distance of the flight, the sensors to be carried, and so on.

The Airborne Operations Division of Canada Centre for Remote Sensing at present has 4 aircraft in regular use - 1 Falcon, 2 DC-3's and a Convair-580 turboprop. The latter was acquired specifically for radar work and was used among other things in the Sursat programme for underflying the satellite, Seasat, in order to assess its value for surveillance purposes. The synthetic aperture radar operated on X and L bands with both horizontal and vertical polarized radiation; it is now being modified to X and C bands to allow experimental work to be carried out in the 5-7 cm wavelength range. It has a resolution of 1.6 to 3 m which represents the highest resolution performance of any civilian system. Since it was intended to use this aircraft in the Arctic where it would be a long way from base for long periods of time, it would obviously be desirable to be able to process the data on board for immediate observation. This was achieved by the installation of a digital processor designed by MacDonald, Dettwiler and Associates of Vancouver. It allows a quick-look image to be developed on film in real-time and has proved particularly valuable in studying ice conditions.

This quick-look picture is not of such high quality as those processed later but it does not need to be: it gives an immediate overview, which enables the research scientist to spot anything of particular interest and so to plan and modify his project as he goes along. It also means that, where appropriate communication channels exist, he can relay pertinent information to shipping in the area in near real-time.

A block diagram of this arrangement is given in Figure 36. The SAR system transmits and receives signals on the same antenna. To avoid getting them mixed up, a circulator is used which rotates and blocks the transmitter when a system is receiving and blocks the receiver when the system

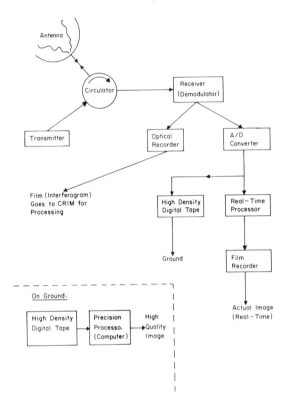

Figure 36. SAR System on Convair-580.

is transmitting. On receiving a return signal the receiver (demodulator) splits the signal into 2 parts. One part goes to the optical recorder and the other to an analogue-to-digital converter. The output from the optical recorder is an interferogram as described in the last chapter, which is later sent to ERIM for processing to a visual image. The second channel is again split into 2 parts after being digitized. One of these parts is recorded on high density digital tape and then taken back to ground for precision processing. This gives an image of very high quality, as may be seen in Figures 52 and 60 to be discussed later. The other channel gives the quick-look image already referred to, which is in the form of a film. Experience with this type of system has shown that digital methods are superior to optical methods in the production of images, and a new radar system is at present being designed in which the optical system is being omitted. This will save space and weight in the aircraft.

The 2 DC-3's have limited range and low speeds and are primarily used for local development work for new sensors, for investigating oil spills, etc. The Falcon is a high speed, high altitude plane suitable for work in the Arctic and has been used notably in support of hydrology programmes.

A number of experimental research projects with these aircraft have been so successful that they have led to fully operational procedures. At this stage C.C.R.S. turns over the routine service work associated with user requests to industry. A new trend is for C.C.R.S. to lease fully-equipped aircraft to industry in order that they may carry out the actual operation. One company which owes its origin to this programme for industrial involvement with airborne projects is Intertech Remote Sensing Ltd. of Ottawa. On the basis of a contract awarded to them in 1975 they have been able to develop an industry–government cooperative relationship that allows research and development activities to continue and also stimulates the conversion of research activities to operational services.

Collecting data by means of aircraft is costly, and developments are taking place in the direction of reducing these costs by the design of suitable mini-RPV's (Remotely Piloted Vehicles). These would combine the experience gained from model airplane technology and satellite sensor technology, and we should be able to provide platforms for specialized applications very much more cheaply. Prototypes weighing under 100 kg. have been designed to fly up to 2200 km. carrying a sensor payload of about 15 kg. They are cheap to launch, easily portable and require little fuel; they would be particularly suitable for operation under hazardous conditions in remote areas.

It is now six or seven centuries since the first primitive rockets were used in warfare. Through the ages their power, range and control have been improved step-by-step until one of the most advanced rockets for war purposes, the V2 rocket of World War II, was developed. At the end of the War numbers of these rockets, as yet fortunately unused for their intended purpose, were found in the hands of the Germans. They were put to good use experimentally by the Russians and the Americans as platforms for scientific instruments to probe the upper layers of atmosphere above the earth. This was really the beginning of our present programmes of space research. Among the most important stages in the development of rockets was first of all the change-over from the use of solid fuels, such as gunpowder, to liquid fuels. One of the first liquid-fuelled rockets was fired in the United States in 1926 by Robert H. Goddard; this feat has been commemorated by naming the central space research station in the States after him - the Goddard Space Flight Centre at Greenbelt, Maryland. Another important stage was the development of multistage rockets; this enabled the rocket to go much higher and to travel further. The range of the earlier rockets was limited because they were so heavy in relation to the amount of fuel they were able to carry. By shedding some of their unwanted weight along the way they were enabled to use their fuel more efficiently. A two-stage rocket, for example, consists of two rockets, one mounted on top of the other. The fuel from one stage is used first to set the whole rocket on its way; when this is finished, the first stage falls away, leaving the second stage carrying the scientific instruments to continue the rest of the journey on its own. it has only a fraction of its original weight and starts off on this stage of its lone journey with a considerable initial speed. When it in turn fires its propellant, it is therefore able to acquire much greater speeds. Larger multistage rockets were soon developed culminating in the well-known Viking series. Large numbers of small rockets have been used, largely in the U.S., for gathering atmospheric and meteorological data and for studying the radiation from the sun and outer space.

These developments were all very interesting and were an important stage in our progress to space research, but a rocket is by no means an ideal platform for surveying the earth, or even for looking at the surrounding atmosphere. To begin with it has to be blasted off the earth at very high accelerations. The shock is liable to damage the instruments it is carrying; it is, in fact, quite amazing to think that delicate instruments can withstand these shocks at all and still go on working. Again when the rocket returns to earth, the impact is liable to cause further damage to the instruments and to the records they have made. The amount and type of information we can get is limited. The rocket goes up and comes down again within a period of a few minutes, and the length of time it may be in exactly the right position to record the data is even less. However, a large number of photographs over a short period of time is possible, and there is the advantage that the lighting conditions over this brief span are uniform. An earth resource rocket has been developed in Britain where it is claimed to have some advantages for specific purposes, such as crop surveys. A rocket lends itself to short-term planning; it can be held at the launching site in readiness for just the right moment when the clouds pass and then released under the control of its operator.

In general, though, the rocket provides a rather expensive way of collecting information. We can use the advances in rocketry more effectively by using them to put satellites into orbit. Prolonged measurements of the earth from space can be carried out only with satellites, either manned or unmanned, and we will take here as an example the satellite which was put into orbit by the U.S. in July, 1972. It was originally called ERTS-1 (Earth Resource Technology Satellite), and the images taken from it for the first years were labelled with ERTS nomenclature. On January 14, 1975, it was renamed Landsat-1, and so there is sometimes a little confusion in the records. Landsat-1 was planned as the first of a series and was primarily designed not so much to collect data for its own sake (although the data collected has in fact exceeded all expectations), but rather to test the feasibility of doing so and the value of such data. The nations of the world were invited by the National Aeronautics and Space Administration (NASA) to take part in this experiment. Canada accepted the challenge and has been receiving data from this satellite or subsequent ones ever since. Since several later satellites were modified forms of Landsat-1, we will look at this in some detail. However before doing so we will consider the properties of satellites in general -- their behaviour, speeds, heights and orbits.

It is rather amazing when we realise that such an apparently exotic body as an artificial satellite behaves according to the laws of motion propounded by Sir Isaac Newton in the middle of the seventeenth century. Everyone has heard the story of how Isaac Newton, as a young man of 23, was sitting in his garden under a tree when an apple fell nearby, and how he was immediately inspired with the theory of gravitation. Actually at the time Newton was studying the motions of the heavenly bodies at Cambridge. He happened to be home because the plague which was rampant at that time had caused the authorities to close the University.

About 50 years earlier Johannes Kepler, dealing mathematically with a mass of meticulously recorded data left by his teacher and mentor, the Danish astronomer Tycho Brahe, had already taken a big step in enunciating certain laws with respect to the movements of the planets. These were the facts, but what about the explanation? It was typical of the originality of Newton's mind that while the obvious question seemed to be "Why doesn't the moon fall to earth? What holds it up there?" Newton was saying "Why doesn't the moon fly off into outer space? What holds it close to earth?" He had already outlined his laws of motion in which he said: "A body will continue to move at the same speed in the same direction unless some outside force acts on it." Why then did the moon not continue in a straight line? Why did it take a circular path round the earth? There must be some mysterious force acting on it and pulling it earthwards. What was it? In watching the apple falling to the ground Newton realised that the force which caused the apple to fall to earth was the same force that kept the moon hugging the earth instead of shooting off into space. This force of attraction between two bodies he called Gravitation, and this is the force which keeps our satellites in orbit.

The moon is a natural satellite of earth, travelling round it in an almost circular path at an average distance of about 385,000 km, or 239,000 miles. It is subject to exactly the same laws of mechanics as any other body. The artificial satellites which we are now placing in orbit are also subject to these same laws. Had we been able to launch such a satellite three centuries ago, Newton would have been able to tell us all about the relation between its height and the speed with which it would have travelled round its orbit (i.e. its orbital speed as opposed to the speed with which it travels outward from the earth). He could have predicted the height at which we should place it in order for it to complete any given number of orbits a day. He predicted an escape velocity for a rocket, that is, the speed a rocket must acquire in order for it to overcome the gravitational attraction of the earth and escape into outer space. This speed is a little over 11 km per second (about 7 miles per second). The only difference really between then and now is that now we have the means of attaining these high speeds; we have the propellants and we have the materials to withstand the high stresses caused by the initial firing. We can design multistage rockets to launch our vehicles into space.

Newton's theories of the movements of the celestial bodies showed that the speed with which such a body circles the earth is related to its distance from the earth - the further it is away the slower it will travel. The speed, in fact, varies as the reciprocal of the square root of its height. This knowledge allows an engineer to design an orbit for a satellite to travel around the earth, say 14 times a day, as was done in the case of Landsat. For this it is necessary for it to travel about 918 km (570 miles) up. He can even design an orbit such that a satellite keeps pace with the earth turning on its axis; in this way it would appear to hang stationary in the sky. This is called a *geostationary orbit*; for this the satellite has to be placed very high above the equator, at a distance of about 35,400 to 37,000 km (22,000 to 23,000 miles). It will then take 24 hours to circle the globe, but, since the earth also completes one rotation in this time, it will appear to us to stand still.

In designing the paths of artificial satellites there are three main types of orbits. One is the *geostationary orbit* just mentioned; another is a *polar orbit* in which the satellite travels from North to South, or South to North over the poles; and another is an *inclined orbit* in which the plane of the orbit makes an angle with the polar plane of the earth. These are shown diagrammatically in Figure 37.

Landsat traveled in a near-polar, sun-synchronous orbit. it traveled from North to South in daylight hours and from South to North at night. The fact that it was sun-synchronous means that it crossed the equator at exactly the same local time on every pass no matter over what part of the world it was. This time was designed to be 9.30 a.m.

Platforms

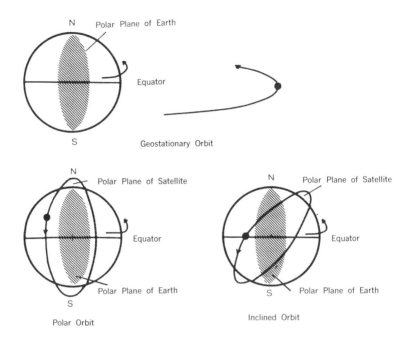

Figure 37. Types of Satellite orbits around the Earth.

when some shadows would be evident on the underlying ground. Shadows help to show up the topographical features more clearly. By passing over at exactly the same time every day the sensors would be assured of looking at the ground below and photographing the scenes under conditions of light and shade as similar as possible. Of course, there would be differences caused by different amounts of cloud cover and different seasons of the year, but this is something over which we have no control.

Landsat completed 14 orbits a day and so took 103.3 minutes to go completely round the earth. You may say "If the satellite crossed the equator 14 times in a 24 hour period how did it always do so at the same time?" The answer is that it was the same *local* time, or the same *sun* time. In the period between successive passes (i.e. about 103 minutes) the earth itself had rotated and the time zones with it. The earth makes one complete rotation a day, during which time the satellite spun around from pole to pole 14 times. Actually it is easier for us to think of the earth as being still and the plane of orbit of the satellite as moving around it as depicted in Figure 38.

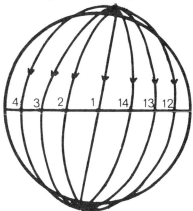

Figure 38. Landsat Orbits for a 24-hour Period.

The earth's circumference is about 40,050 km (29,900 miles); successive orbits would therefore step off distances of about 2870 km round the equator. Near the poles the distances would be much shorter and the swaths of land swept out by the scanning sensors would overlap. We can therefore think of the earth as an enormous orange with 14 sections; the satellite passes over each section twice a day, once in the day (downwards) and once at night (upwards).

It is rather difficult to imagine these rotations in three dimensions, so let us open up this spherical globe and lay it out flat as is done in an atlas with a Mercator projection. We will consider one day in the life of Landsat-I, and we will plot the ground trace for each orbit (i.e. the position of the ground immediately below the satellite, its nadir point). These paths may be seen in Figure 39.

We will imagine that day 1 started when the satellite was somewhere in the Pacific Ocean at latitude 0. It passed approximately over the South pole and up again on the other side of the earth. At that time the other side of the earth was in darkness, and so we are not really interested in its path. 103 minutes later the satellite would pass in a North to South direction over the equator again, but by this time the earth would have moved under it from West to East and the sun time would be the same. This was repeated, as you

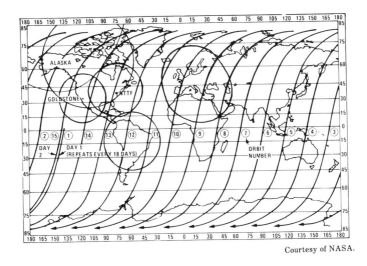

Courtesy of NASA.

Figure 39. Typical Landsat Daily Ground Trace (daylight passes only).

can see from the diagram, 14 times and the satellite was
then ready in position to start another day's work. The first
orbit the next day would be number 15, but you will notice
that it does not exactly coincide with orbit number 1. The
reason is this: on the equator the distance between
successive orbits was 2870 km, but the sensors on board the
satellite were scanning a ribbon of terrain only 185 km wide.
This means that there were large areas of land between
these passes which were not being looked at. On the second
day therefore all the ground traces were pushed just a little
ahead of the previous positions; on the third day a little
further still, until, at the end of the eighteenth day, the
whole globe had been covered. You can see that at the end
of this period the last trace (i.e. orbit number 252) would
coincide with the first trace of the first day. The whole
cycle then started over again, so that the first orbit of the
nineteenth day fell exactly over the second orbit of the first
day, and subsequent orbits also repeated themselves. In this
way every part of the globe was covered once every
eighteen days. Closer to the poles, where there was so
much overlap, coverage was more frequent. Figure 40
shows an enlargement of the ground traces between orbits 1
and 2 of the first day. 1 is the first orbit of the first day
1/1; 15 represents the first orbit of the second day 1/2; 29

represents the first orbit of the third day 1/3, and so on, until we reach orbit 253 which represents the first orbit of the nineteenth day 1/19, which coincides with the second orbit of the first day.

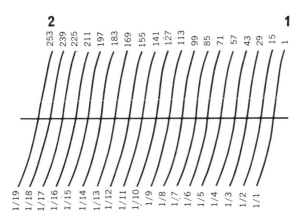

Figure 40. Ground Traces for the First Orbit of each Day in an 18-day Cycle.

As we have said, on the equator successive orbits were 2870 km apart; this distance was covered by seventeen intermediate ground traces; the width between each of these traces was therefore 160 km. The sensors recorded a swath of 185 km. so that there was a sidelap of nearly 16% at the equator; because of the convergence of the tracks at the poles there was a sidelap of about 90% at higher latitudes. This may appear redundant, but it must be remembered that not all the scenes would have been good ones; some may have been useless because of cloud cover. It is fortunate for Canada that there is this overlap because the Arctic regions are of particular interest to us.

We have said that Landsat-1 traveled in a *near*-polar orbit. Why was it only near-polar? If it had been exactly polar we would not have been able to make it sun-synchronous throughout the year because of a phenomenon known as precession. The angle required for this in the case of Landsat-1 at a height of about 900 km. was 9°. Its coverage of the earth was therefore not quite complete but extended from 81° N. to 81° S. and certainly contained most of the areas we are interested in. This is the way Landsat

traveled. How about the satellite itself? What did it look
like?

Landsat weighed a little over 90 kg; it was about 3 m
high and 1.5 m in diameter. Figure 41 shows what it looked
like.

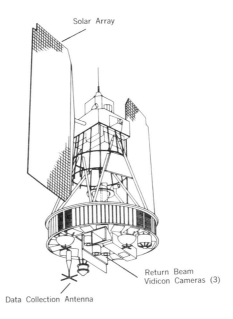

Figure 41. Diagram of Landsat-1.

As has already been discussed, Landsat-1 carried on
board two sensors; one was a return beam vidicon system
containing three cameras, and this can be seen attached to
the base; the other was the multispectral scanner. Each of
these had its own high-density tape recorder. The output
from the vidicons was transmitted to earth in analogue form
by radio at a frequency of 2265.5 MHz. The output from the
multispectral scanner was recorded in digital form and
transmitted to earth at a frequency of 2229.5 MHz. Data
was not transmitted continuously but only when the satellite
was within view of a ground receiving station. It would have
been a waste of energy to be sending out signals over the
other side of the world where there were no ground stations

to receive them, and energy is at a premium in a satellite. The transmission was therefore switched off and the data taped for subsequent play-back on command from a U.S. ground station. By arrangement with NASA, when the satellite was over Canadian territory, the transmission was always switched on, so that all information could be received at the ground station at Prince Albert. The antennas for transmitting this data can be seen at the base. In addition to sending out the information which its own sensors had gathered, the satellite could relay the information which it received from the data collection platforms on earth, as was mentioned at the beginning of the chapter. This allowed users to obtain this earth-based data without having to visit impenetrable and inaccessible regions in the middle of winter, and without the expense of land-based communication systems.

For her part Canada had to provide only the facilities for handling remote-sensing data. The U.S., on the other hand, had to concern itself with a number of other factors, and several other channels of communication were necessary. Once the satellite was put into orbit, checks had to be made constantly on its position; if it was found to be out of orbit, adjustments had to be made. This was achieved by a monopropellant hydrazine subsystem employing one-pound-force thrusters; it was able to provide the force necessary for correcting the orbit on launching and also for making any necessary adjustments as might have been necessary afterwards. The attitude of the spacecraft had to be maintained so that it was always looking straight down to earth. An attitude control subsystem was installed that kept the vertical axis within 0.7° of the true vertical. The pitch and roll was corrected by means of an instrument which scanned the horizon on all sides, fed back any errors in position and allowed corrections to be made. A gyro compass corrected for yaw.

For all these tasks the satellite required electrical power, which it had to get from the sun. Figure 40 shows two independent solar arrays. These are banks of silicon photovoltaic cells which are able to convert sunlight into electricity. A near-polar orbiter such as Landsat-1, which traveled in the dark for about half of its journey, had to have some means of storing its power; this storage was provided by the batteries, which were drawn on as needed and recharged when the satellite was in sunlight.

Landsat-1, was launched into orbit in July, 1972, and was finally retired in January, 1978. Although the RBV's ceased to function soon after launch, the wealth of data provided over an almost six-year period proved the experiment to have been spectacularly successful. The imagery obtained almost immediately was better than hoped for, and more modern methods of enhancement and analysis are still providing information from the original tapes and will no doubt continue to do so for some time to come.

Landsat-1 was the first of a series. Since its initiation, other members of the series have been brought into action with some minor design modifications. Before launch each satellite bears the letter A, B, C, etc. After launch this nomenclature is changed to a numerical sequence, 1, 2, 3, etc. ERTS-A began its life in space as ERTS-1 and was later changed to Landsat-1. ERTS-B became Landsat-2 on attaining orbit in January, 1975, and Landsat-C became Landsat-3 when it was launched in March, 1978.

Landsat-2 was identical in payload to Landsat-1 and, despite a design lifetime of only one year, it continued to function satisfactorily for five years. At that time failure of its primary flight control mechanism became evident, and it was difficult to keep the spacecraft looking towards the earth. Landsat-3 is now continuing as the sole member of the Landsat series still in orbit. When it was launched in 1978 Landsat-2 was still operating, and it was arranged that the 18-day repeat period for each satellite would overlap so as to give repetitive coverage of any given area every 9 days. This proved of great value in the surveillance of dynamic events, and gave an idea of what might happen in the future when perhaps several such satellites will be launched to give almost daily coverage.

Landsat-3 carried a multispectral scanner with four bands identical to those of Landsat-1 and Landsat-2. It also carried a fifth band in the thermal infrared (10.4 - 12.6 m), but unfortunately this failed shortly after launch. Since in previous satellites the multispectral scanner had proved so good with regard to spectral differentiation, the RBV cameras were relieved of their responsibility to provide colour and were able to concentrate on improved spatial resolution, which has proved valuable for mapping purposes. Therefore instead of 3 cameras with 3 different spectral filters, Landsat-3 carried 2 panchromatic cameras each having a broadband spectral response of 505 - 750 nanometres. Each camera gave twice the ground resolution (40m) of those on Landsat-1 and Landsat-2; this was achieved by doubling the focal length of the lens system. The two cameras were mounted side by side so that each could view a 98 km square area of ground. Adjacent areas overlapped by 14 km and so together formed a pair 183 x 98 km. The cameras were shuttered to operate twice as fast as those in the two previous satellites. As a consequence, in the frame which was originally 185 m square we then had 4 sub-frames 98 m square with a ground resolution of 40 m. A limited amount of RBV data has been received by the Prince Albert station which will be discussed further in the next chapter. It has been converted to annotated quick-look images. The standard 9-inch image had a scale of approximately 1:500,000.

The series is now being continued with the launching of Landsat-4 in 1982. The payload of this satellite includes a multispectral scanner and a thematic mapper, as will be discussed further in Chapter IX. A more accurate location of the satellite in space will be provided by a Global Positioning System.

As the name implies, the Landsat series proved to be particularly successful for studying land features. On June 26, 1978 a new experimental satellite, Seasat-I, was launched primarily designed to test the methods most suitable for oceanographic work. Since most of the instruments aboard this satellite operated in the microwave region, Seasat-I was capable of operating in all weathers both day and night. Its near-polar orbit was about 800 km above the earth and the spacecraft circled the earth 14 times a day, allowing its instruments to sweep across 95% of the ocean surface every 36 hours. Its path was slightly more inclined than that of Landsat with the result that the maximum latitude for data collection was 72°. After only four months of operation the satellite unfortunately failed. However, because of its ability to get useable data in all weathers and at night, the amount of data received during that short period of time was considerable. Engineers and scientists will probably be occupied for many years to come in processing the data.

Seasat-I carried four microwave instruments as already described in the last chapter, namely a synthetic aperture radar, an altimeter, a scatterometer, and a microwave radiometer. It also carried a visible/infrared radiometer. The latter sensor was really a support instrument designed to provide ancillary data for the microwave systems. The visible and near infrared part of the sensor, operating at a wavelength range from 490 to 940 nanometres, provided imagery of ocean and coastal features and of clouds. The far infrared section, operating at a wavelength range of 10.5 to 12.5 μ m, was able to detect cloudfree sea surface temperature boundaries.

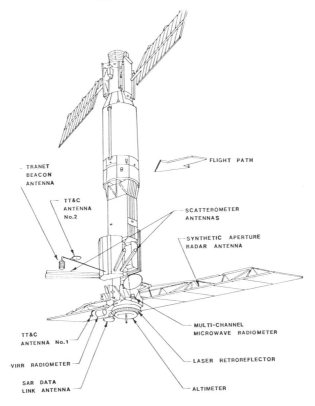

Figure 42. Diagram of Seasat-1.

Of the four microwave sensors the synthetic aperture radar was the one of most interest to us. This was the first time a radar system had been put into orbit in the Landsat/Seasat series, and it provided the data for imagery of almost unbelievable clarity and resolution. The antenna system, 2.1 m by 10.7 m in size, may be seen at the base of the satellite as shown in Figure 42. In flight it looked at a swath of land 100 km wide to give a resolution of 25 m, a resolution considerably better than that obtainable by Landsat instruments (even the RBV's of Landsat-3 would give a resolution of only 40 m). The antenna beamed a 1.275 GHz radar signal to earth and after reflection the returned signal was amplified, converted to a frequency of 2.265 GHz and telemetered to the tracking station in analogue form, where it was converted to digital form and taped. A block diagram showing the overall scheme of reception and processing of the returned signal is shown in Figure 46.

The demands placed on the power supplies of the spacecraft were considerable. Not all the instruments were operating all the time. Normal requirements varied from about 500 to 700 watts, but could exceed 1,200 watts during brief periods of radar operation. All this power had to be provided by large solar collectors seen at the top of the spacecraft. The collector system consisted of two rotatable 11-panel solar arrays, capable of generating about 1000 watts. Two nickel-cadmium storage batteries were used for providing power in the early stages before the solar panel had had time to collect any energy from the sun, for storing energy for peak power requirements and for operating during a solar eclipse.

The combined weight of all these instruments was also considerable and posed some design problems. The SAR weighed 147 kg, the radar altimeter 93.8 kg, the scatterometer 59 kg, the microwave radiometer 54 kg and the visual and infrared radiometer 8.0 kg for a total of nearly 500 kg; to which, of course, must be added the weight of the spacecraft itself and the equipment for communicating with the earth and for keeping it in its prescribed orbit.

The opportunity offered to Canada to take part in Landsat and Seasat programmes enabled this country to gain experience in space technology. It became obvious that satellites have much to commend them as a means of regularly surveilling the earth's surface; they can carry out their mission more cheaply and more effectively than aircraft, although aircraft are still important for obtaining more detail over smaller areas. It is not easy to keep track of what is going on up in the Arctic, for example, where so much exploration and development are taking place, and the extension of jurisdictional limits to 370 km off-shore have stressed the need for continuous surveillance.

The question became, "Which of all the sensors available would best suit our purpose?" It is obvious that we need information on a regular basis and as frequently as possible. The fact that in northern areas daylight hours are very short, almost non-existent in winter, would make microwave methods almost mandatory. The Seasat project presented an opportunity to assess the performance of radar systems from the point of view of surveillance applications. A special program was set up for this purpose, the Canadian Surveillance Satellite Program (SURSAT), and its primary purpose was to determine the role of satellites as part of a total surveillance system which would include aircraft, ships and other vehicles. A secondary aim was to facilitate research into the interpretation of data obtained from microwave sensors and to assess the value of such methods for disciplines such as agriculture, geology and hydrology. To assist them in their task, the SURSAT office asked the many scientific communities across Canada (government, universities and industries) to submit proposals for experiments. The results of many of these experiments will be dealt with in later chapters.

The general conclusion reached was that the value of synthetic aperture radar in a spacecraft had been proved beyond doubt, especially when backed-up by further information obtained from airborne radar. The system is capable of providing high resolution imagery from space for surveillance purposes under all weather conditions. For an operational system a high frequency of coverage would be needed as might be provided by several satellites in suitably adjusted and timed orbits. It would also be necessary to develop faster methods of extracting information from radar data. Digital processing methods were shown to be superior to optical processing as regards resolution, but at present they are rather slow. Future developments in this area will be interesting to watch. Satellites are expensive to construct and launch, but, once launched, worldwide information can be collected quickly and cheaply. It is good to see that several countries are moving towards cooperative efforts in this respect. The European Space Agency (ESA) is drawing together the nations of Europe to pool their experience and resources for launching a combined satellite; Canada is starting a radar satellite programme and is looking at ways of sharing its developments with other agencies.

Although meteorological satellites are really outside the scope of this book, we should perhaps take a brief look at some of them, since they were the forerunners of the more recent earth resource satellites. Despite the fact that they were designed for observation of the atmosphere, they represent man's first attempt at recording earth's data from space; while the resolution of the early ones was too poor to allow much information to be gathered on the earth itself, more recent developments have led to such improvement that they can now serve the dual purpose of weather-forecasting and small-scale earth mapping. This makes them particularly useful for surveying large areas of ice to show its disposition and movement.

T.V. cameras and scanning radiometers in the later Tiros, Essa, and Nimbus satellites have shown useful imagery of sea-ice conditions. The Nimbus-5 satellite is of special interest to us in this respect; it carried a scanning microwave radiometer operating at a wavelength of 1.55 cm. giving a spatial resolution of about 30 km and provided daily global coverage of sea ice distribution. With this satellite, views of the entire polar regions have been obtained showing brightness temperatures of these areas. One such photograph is shown in Plate II. A more recent satellite in the Nimbus series, Nimbus-7, has added a type of multispectral scanner to its complement of instruments. Called a Coastal Zone Colour Scanner (CACS) this 6-channel instrument senses the temperature and colour of coastal waters, which in turn gives information on water quality.

The late NOOA satellites with their very high resolution radiometers (VHRR) have also proved invaluable for the mapping of sea-ice and give a resolution of approximately 1 km immediately below the satellite. This is considerably poorer resolution than that given by Landsat, and you may wonder that we should refer to the radiometer as having very high resolution. The reason is that NOAA is primarily a class of meteorological satellites and the resolution is considerably higher than that of preceding meteorological satellites. The satellite travels in a near-polar, sun-synchronous orbit at an altitude of 1450 km and is thus able to give wide coverage twice a day instead of once every 18 days. This makes it useful for studying ice movements where the delineation of large masses is required rather than the details of individual floes.

If so much information can be obtained from an unmanned satellite, how much more could we expect by putting men into it to operate the instruments? The whole programme immediately becomes much more flexible. Scientists could carry out short or long term experiments, could make repairs in transit, or instal new equipment; they could bring the data back to earth in person; they might be able to release small satellites from their spaceship as the occasion demanded.

This then was the next major step – a laboratory in the sky. And so on May 13, 1973, Skylab was launched. It was put into an inclined orbit at 50° to the equator. With such an angle of inclination it was possible to obtain coverage only between latitudes 50° N and 50° S, so that unfortunately not very much of Canada was included. The spacecraft itself was at a rather lower altitude than Landsat – about 270 miles up instead of 567 miles; consequently it rotated more quickly and completed its orbit in 93.2 minutes as against 103.3 minutes for Landsat. When on February 8, 1974, the last astronauts left their temporary home in the sky, Skylab had carried her crews a total of 70 million miles and had circled the globe 2,476 times. The ground trace patterns for the Skylab orbits are shown in Figure 43. Skylab was not designed primarily for looking at the earth as was Landsat; this was really only quite a small part of its mission. Altogether more than 250 experiments were carried out. Their objectives were firstly to study the behaviour of man and other living creatures under space conditions (medical, biological and psychological studies); secondly to study intergalactic space and the celestial

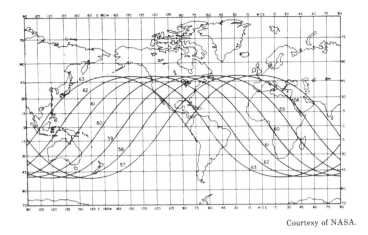

Courtesy of NASA.

Figure 43. Ground Trace Pattern for Skylab.

bodies, particularly the sun; thirdly to collect data on the earth and its atmosphere as had been done by the unmanned satellites. In addition a series of other scientific investigations were carried out, among them experiments on the growing of crystals and the alloying of metals under conditions of low gravity.

An account of all these experiments would fill several books in themselves; the only ones we can even glimpse at here are the earth resource studies because, in a way, they were a follow-up to those carried out with Landsat-I. The time allotted to these studies was limited, but it did allow an assessment to be made of a number of new sensors, and again a whole lot of new data was made available for later interpretation.

You remember that Landsat carried only two sensors - a return beam vidicon system and a multispectral scanner. Skylab had a more ambitious payload. The multispectral scanner covered 10 wavelength ranges in the visible range, two in the near infrared and one in the thermal infrared. This is a total of 13 channels as against 4 in Landsat. The lower wavelength limit was 400 nanometers in the violet as against 500 nanometres in the blue-green for Landsat. We really don't need 13 bands to delineate most boundaries, but we would like to know which is the best for any particular purpose. A comparison of the information gained from all these regions should tell us this. As well as small hand cameras held by the astronauts themselves, Skylab carried 6 other photographic cameras. Four of these used black and white film but operated in different wavelength regions through four different filters; one used colour-infrared film and the other ordinary colour film. All of them were arranged to look at the same area of ground about 79 metres square (260 feet square) so that a valid comparison could be made. The contact scale of these photographs was 1:2,800,000.

Microwave sensors were also carried. An active system was used for measuring the microwave reflectivity of ground objects, and also a passive system operating at various wavelengths for recording emitted radiation. Finally a view-finder-spectrometer capable of spectral scanning was included in the package to allow the recording of visible and infrared spectral signatures of earth objects. The ground coverage could be changed from a diameter of about 11.3 to 113 km (7 to 70 miles) by a zoom lens system.

This represents a truly impressive collection of sensors which were brought to bear on our small planet. Whenever possible lower altitude records from planes were also obtained simultaneously in order to give ground truth data and help in the subsequent intrepretation of Skylab records. None of the information was telemetered to earth during flight. The photographic film was brought back by each crew on return to earth; the non-photographic data was taped on high density tape and brought back in the same way.

Plans are now going ahead for the launching of a permanent sky laboratory to be staffed by scientists travelling to and fro in a space shuttle. This sky platform will enable experiments to be carried out in space. The preliminary stages, including trips by the space shuttle, Columbia, have already proved successful, and it is hoped to bring the whole programme into operation in the latter half of this decade.

An important contribution was made by Canada in the design and manufacture of the Canadarm, an automatic extensible arm which may be manipulated robot-fashion from inside. It will be used for handling cargo and moving scientific equipment into position outside the orbiter. It might also be useful for launching and retrieving small satellites.

Canadian scientists are joining with scientists from other Pacific Rim countries, such as the U.S. and Australia in the planning of a new instrument for space research, STARLAB, a 1 m telescope equipped with a camera and spectrograph. This would be carried in the sky laboratory and, having a large field of view, would be used to examine minute objects in space.

CHAPTER V

RECEIVING THE DATA ON EARTH

We have now seen how data can be sent from the earth to the aircraft or satellite, how it is recorded there and how it is sent back again to earth. We will now take a look at what happens next - how this data is received and interpreted and the information disseminated to those who wish to make use of it.

The problem of recovering data from aircraft is relatively simple; the volume is less, and some selection of scenes has already taken place. The aircraft records data only at a specific demand, at a specific place and when weather conditions are suitable. Whoever requests a flight knows exactly what it is he is looking for. With an unmanned satellite, on the other hand, there is no such selection. Data is gathered on a continuous basis; the customers wishing to make use of it are legion and their interests varied. A tremendous volume of material is gathered and we run the risk of being snowed under with tapes, photographs, charts and signals, all of which have to be interpreted, assessed, and routed as quickly as possible. Sometimes the material is useless unless it can be conveyed to the right person within a few hours.

The organization and handling of all this data is a stupendous task. But, first of all, how do we actually receive it on earth?

Taking Landsat as an example, we see that the satellite is gathering data from all over the world, but there are as yet only a few stations capable of receiving it. Originally there were three stations in the U.S., namely at Fairbanks, Alaska; at Goldstone, California; and at the Goddard Space Flight Centre at Greenbelt, Maryland. There was a station in Canada at Prince Albert, Saskatchewan.

Probably the simplest way of describing just how the data is received is to look at an actual ground receiving station. As an example we will take Canada's receiving station at Prince Albert.

When Canada made the decision in the late 1960's to cooperate with NASA in investigating the potential of satellites for studying the earth's natural resources, the first thing to consider was where a receiving station should be built. As this would be necessarily of an experimental nature, it was desirable to spend as little money as possible consistent with good reception; it would be bad policy to put the taxpayer to unwarranted expense in order to build from scratch an elaborate, permanent installation which might later prove to be a white elephant. It was also desirable to have as complete a coverage as possible of the whole of Canada and particularly of the Arctic region. Data on this area has been woefully lacking because of its inaccessibility, and the lack is being keenly felt at this time of rapid expansion. Another requirement was to bring the station into operation quickly so that it would be ready to receive data as soon as Landsat-1 was launched. Compromises had to be made. The final decision was made to build this station at Prince Albert, Saskatchewan. The fact that such successful results have been achieved in so short a time speaks very highly of the skill and enthusiasm of those involved.

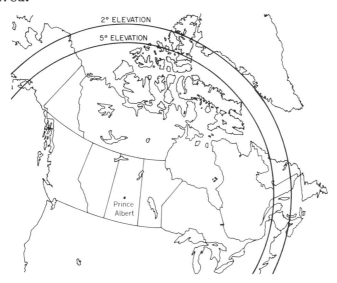

Figure 44. Landsat Coverage from Ground Station at Prince Albert.

Figure 44 shows the area which was expected to be covered by the receiving station at Prince Albert. In actual practice the area has turned out to be a little larger than this. You can see that the coverage for Canada is quite good, though not complete. It does not include the whole of Ellesmere Island or the whole of the Atlantic Provinces.

In 1978 a second Canadian station was installed at Shoe Cove, Newfoundland, which covers the Atlantic Provinces and, in fact, about 500 km out into the Atlantic Ocean. This station also receives and processes Landsat and NOAA data and was later modified to accept transmissions from Seasat.

Landsat completes its coverage of the whole world from East to West in 18 days. Since it executes 14 orbits from North to South in a day, and since on each successive day the orbits are stepped slightly forward, the final one of the 18th day coincides in path with the first orbit of the first day; it is clear that the world is covered by 251 orbits (i.e. 14 x 18 -1).

During the summer Landsat is within range of Prince Albert Satellite Station for at least part of over 80 of these 251 orbits; in the longest days of the season 81 orbits have been tracked in an 18–day period. During the winter as the days become shorter this number is reduced.

We can calculate the length of time the satellite is over Canadian territory. We find that in the summer months PASS can receive information for 34 to 40 minutes a day. This will be the total for 5 or 6 passes. In the winter this time is reduced to 15 or 32 minutes depending on the month and the day.

Is it not surprising what a great deal of data can be received in so short a time? This is due to the very high speed at which the data can be picked up and transmitted to earth.

Of course, all the images are not necessarily useful. Sometimes the clouds are so dense that the satellite cannot "see" the earth. During the winter months parts of northern Canada are in darkness, but in other parts there may be too much light. Snow has a very high reflectance and it may happen that too much light is thrown into the sensors; this might have the unhappy effect, we might say, of blinding them. As we know, we ourselves can become blinded by the brilliant light from the snow in the bright days of March, and the same thing can happen with instruments; they become saturated.

Courtesy of Canada Centre for Remote Sensing

Figure 45. Receiving Antenna at Prince Albert.

The heart of the receiving system is a large parabolic dish antenna, such as you can see at many places around the countryside where it is used for radar reception and transmission. In fact, the Prince Albert station was originally used for radar and required only minor adjustments to adapt it to its present use. You can see an illustration of this in Figure 45. The antenna is 25 m in diameter and is also used to receive DCP (data collection platform) signals from various locations in Canada and relay them to earth.

So, in simple form, we have signals sent out from the satellite, collected by the receiver at the centre of the parabolic reflector, and carried down the antenna tower to the control room where they are recorded.

In order to get good pictures and ones which can be compared from orbit to orbit, it is of course necessary that the antenna should be "looking" at the satellite dead on.

To make sure that the PASS antenna is looking straight at the satellite and follows or tracks it correctly over that part of its orbit in which we are interested, two separate tracking systems are used. One is a computer-driven system which puts the antenna right on target and then locks it into a second system, which enables it to track automatically.

If you visit the receiving station at Prince Albert (and you will certainly be made welcome if you do) you can see the large parabolic reflector slowly moving across the sky, automatically following an unseen satellite. You will know that it is in the process of receiving information from aloft, and, if you go inside the small buildings beside it, you will be able to see some of these messages being flashed on to a screen. They may not seem to make much sense to the uninitiated eye, but to those in command the squiggles and flashes portrayed there mean a great deal. How may all this data be interpreted?

We saw earlier that the return beam vidicon of Landsat-1 & 2 virtually took snapshots of the earth in three wavelength bands (1, 2 and 3) corresponding to the colours green, red and near infrared. Each one covered an area on the ground of 185 km by 185 km (115 miles square) and there was an overlap of each one of about 10%. These images were collected on a sort of TV screen in the satellite as already described. The picture was then scanned with an electron beam, the information picked off it, taped, and converted into analogue video signals, similar to a normal T.V. signal, and transmitted to earth at a frequency of 2265 MHz. After frequency-changing and amplification these signals were led down the antenna tower into the control room, digitized and recorded on high-density 28-track magnetic tape. After taping, the tape could be used to throw an image of the ground scene on a high resolution cathode ray tube, where it could be looked at to check that everything was working correctly, or it could be photographed. This cathode ray tube had very high demands placed on it, so that full use could be made of the high resolution capabilities of the RBV system. The image was made up of 4500 lines, each with 4500 picture elements, and this is far beyond the ability of any ordinary TV tube with 525 lines to reproduce. A special tube therefore had to be developed for this purpose. In Landsat-3 an RBV with double the resolution is used with black and white data only, so that the reception and recording has been considerably simplified.

The other sensing system, the multispectral scanner, required rather more complicated receiving equipment. Instead of only three different traces for the three different spectral bands, the MSS had four such bands, including an extra one in the near infrared. Also it did not take "snapshots" of a whole area, but swept an area continuously from side to side. You remember that across the direction of travel the area swept out is divided into 6 separate contiguous tracks, each of which is recorded on 4 separate detectors corresponding to the 4 separate wavebands. There are therefore 24 separate records which have to be made, and this fact again means extra complications in converting the information to a format which is suitable for presentation to a cathode ray tube. In the spacecraft the output of each trace is sampled in sequence, put in digital form, then scrambled or multiplexed into a single signal and sent to the ground. On reception this has to be unscrambled, or demultiplexed, before it can be converted into a meaningful image. It is recorded on a high speed 28-track tape and the image may be thrown onto a screen and photographed. But here we run into a little difficulty. Whereas the images from the RBV were fairly simple to photograph, being of the single exposure variety, those of the MSS would be depicted as from a continuous ribbon and this is not a convenient form for viewing imagery. A photograph is therefore taken of an area 185 m square. The film is then automatically moved on to a new position; this is repeated every 25 seconds. However the MSS pictures leave a little out because of the time taken in moving the film, but this amounts only to something less than 1%; if there appears to be anything of special interest in the missing area, it is easy to replay the tape shifting the image slightly so as to include that portion which was previously missing.

As you might guess, this description of the receiving process has been somewhat oversimplified. In practice it is subject to several errors for which allowances have to be made. It is easy to understand that the geometric errors and distortions are likely to be much more serious in the case of MSS images than in those from the RBV. The latter are taken in a brief instant of time, so that any movement of the spacecraft would not affect them to any very great extent. In the case of the MSS the collection of data is a slower process. It was earlier feared that such factors as yaw, pitch and roll of the satellite, as well as the movement during its continuous passage over the earth, might lead to distortion and lack of clarity in the final picture. This fortunately has not been borne out in practice. The RBV of Landsat-I was shut off due to power troubles about 30 to 35 days after launch, but Canada managed to get some data from it, and then had to depend on MSS data alone. These images turned out to be so much better than had been expected that the loss of the RBV was of little consequence. However, some errors are inherent in the system, but in most cases they can be corrected for. We will look at the nature of some of these and see how they affect the images received.

First, we have to remember that in the case of the MSS, while the scanning mirror is oscillating from side to side and sweeping out a swath of earth below it, the satellite itself is moving from North to South. At the same time the earth is moving under it from West to East. In the short time that the scanner collects the information the earth's movement is not very great, but, nevertheless, it is sufficient to displace the resulting image; however this is a known and constant effect and so can be corrected for in processing.

Secondly there is the attitude of the spacecraft. It may not always be quite horizontal and so may not be looking squarely at the earth. There is a correction mechanism in the satellite itself which holds the tilting angle below 0.7°, but even this small deviation is significant in that it leads to a displacement of the resulting image. This can be partly corrected for by information given by the satellite itself. In the case of the MSS system, because of the time taken to carry out a scan, the error may not be constant over the whole of the picture; this would result in geometric distortion. Accurate corrections can be made by comparing the relative positions of some outstanding features on the photograph with those same features on an accurate map. Errors due to rotation of the satellite may be calculated in the same way.

As we know, the earth is round and this leads to small projection errors. These, however, are constant and are known and so can be corrected for. Actually, the presentation of a spherical globe on a flat piece of paper is an artificial process at best; most maps are drawn according to the well-known Mercator projection method, and we have become so accustomed to seeing our world portrayed in this way that we accept it. Landsat and other spacecraft, you might say, merely provide us with a new projection. It is just as valid as any other, but we are not used to it and find it difficult to visualize. Perhaps with increasing use of images from space we shall later find that we do not need to alter the original data; with experience we will become accustomed to the new projection and will accept this as one among the others. In fact, it is very difficult to distinguish one projection from another over an area covered by a single satellite image. Recently a new technique has been developed which will allow all imagery from any satellite to be corrected and brought to a common format, so that images from Landsat, Seasat, etc. may be directly compared and overlaid. The instrument for carrying out this process is the Digital Image Correction System (DICS) and will be discussed further in Chapter VI.

These errors which we have been discussing are what we might call geometric errors. There is one other type of error which we must consider and this is one due to variations in the response of the sensors themselves. These are called radiometric errors. The response of any image-forming device may vary with time; in particular, it may decrease as the instrument ages. Since the information given in any picture is in the form of variations of optical density, in other words, darkness or lightness, any non-uniformity of response is important. It is important in comparing day-to-day records and is even more important in producing colour films. In the optical system of the MSS, for example, if the sensor response in one of the wavelength bands falls off, or if one of the filters becomes more opaque and transmits less light, the colour balance of the final picture would be thrown out. Steps are therefore taken to calibrate these instruments, and corrections are made in the light of these results. Other things to be considered are variation due to amplification of the signals, atmospheric transmittance, sun angle, and finally the film and developing process.

Having collected all this data, how can we let the user know what is available? As mentioned before, one of the special features of PASS is its Quick-Look system. This was originally developed to enable the station personnel to have a quick look at the way things were working, to check the quality of the data being received and to make any equipment adjustments that might prove necessary. However it has now developed into a very valuable customer service, which enables anyone interested to get data from the RBV system in the quickest possible time. These preliminary results do not have all the refinements of the final image, but speed is sometimes more important than accuracy, and a quick look may be able to supply all the information required.

Originally MSS data was also supplied as Quick-Look imagery, but it is now handled somewhat differently. The information from the satellite is recorded on the 28-track tape as already mentioned; the output from this tape is fed to a so-called formatter which prepares or reformats the data for display on the CRT. Signals are also fed in which give the reference numbers of the scene on the side. In this way a complete picture of an area 185 km square may be displayed on the screen. At the same time a Multi-Image Processing System (MIPS) performs radiometric and geometric corrections on the data in real time. The corrected data is then passed to a Laser Beam Image Recorder (LBIR), which produces 70 mm corrected negatives for customer use.

These images, produced from both RBV and MSS systems are the basis for sets of microfiche, which are immediately sent out to customers daily. They are available on a subscription basis from C.C.R.S. Prince Albert Receiving Station, Box 1150, Prince Albert, Saskatchewan. Since this service is located on the same site as the receiving station, no time is lost in transporting and processing the tapes and films, and every effort is made to get results to the user as soon as possible.

On receiving his daily collection of microfiche a customer may look at the films with a standard microfilm viewer, and often this will give him all the information he needs. If, however, he would like to see higher quality scenes, he may order the larger 9 inch by 9 inch images. The microfiche can then act as a catalogue of available data and can be permanently filed as such. According to his selection he may order the higher quality images in black and white or as a colour composite to highlight the particular features in which he is interested.

These larger images as well as computer compatible tapes are also available from Prince Albert, or they may be ordered from C.C.R.S., User Assistance and Marketing Unit, 717 Belfast Road, Ottawa, Ontario, K1A 0Y7. This service was initiated to help users find what they want. It may be difficult for newcomers to the remote sensing field to know, first of all, what is available and secondly, how to lay their hands on it, or to order it. Naturally anyone initiating a search should give as much information as possible about the imagery sought. The more you can tell UAMU about your search objectives, the more help they can give. UAMU also maintains files of all Landsat and Seasat products and has some interesting scenes on display. For anyone in Ottawa a visit to Belfast Road might be a rewarding experience.

It is obvious that very quick information can be obtained on changing events. This has already proved of great value to ships at sea fighting severe ice conditions, to the Ice Forecasting Central for their daily ice map records, to foresters for spotting forest fires, to those watching flood situations, and so on. You may well ask "Does this mean that we shall be able to check all forest fires at source?" "Does this mean that we shall be able to get flood information before a flood really gets going?" We must be honest and say "Not always". It is possible if Landsat is in the right place at the right time, but at the crucial moment it may be on the other side of the world and not much good to us. Complete world coverage is at present given only every 18 days, and if a fire were to start just after the satellite had passed the particular spot, an image of that area would not be received for another 18 days. A fire can travel a long way in that time. However by the use of two satellites so phased that the 18 day cycle is shared, it is possible to reduce this to a 9-day repeat period.

So far we have been mainly concerned with the performance of Landsat. Other satellites of the NOAA series, are also yielding some interesting results. These satellites, designed primarily for weather forecasting, carry on board a Very High Resolution Radiometer (VHRR) which operates in two bands, one in the visible red and one in the infrared. A NOAA satellite takes 115 minutes to complete its orbit and PASS is tracking three of these orbits a day. Since the sensor in this satellite has a wide angle lens, it has certain advantages of being able to present a view of a larger area at any given time. This information is being sent daily to the Ice Forecasting Central, to weather forecasting stations, and to any companies that may be interested, and many of them are very much interested. It is also being used to build up a historical record of some areas. Oil companies now exploring Arctic areas would have found it very useful to have had a past record of weather and ice conditions, but we cannot put the clock back; we can, however, ensure that in the future these records will be available. For instance, very little has been known of conditions in the Beaufort Sea area or, in fact, of any area at a latitude north of 60°. We are now building up a fund of information, which should prove of inestimable value to anyone wishing to prospect there in the future.

The Shoe Cove station in Newfoundland was originally built to fill in the reception gap for Landsat over the Canadian Atlantic seaboard. By covering the areas of Greenland and Iceland, it has also been able to provide Landsat data to Danish and Icelandic users. When plans were being considered by NASA for the launching of Seasat, a decision had to be made about the best place for receiving the data from this satellite also. Seasat was primarily designed for oceanographic research. What better place for a ground receiving station than an island with a splendid view of the western reaches of the Atlantic Ocean and with the eastern coastal regions of Canada on its doorstep? Although Seasat would only gather data up to a latitude of 72°, this would include parts of northern Canada and would enable a study to be made of ice-infested waters and snow-covered land.

The Shoe Cove station was therefore modified to make it suitable for the reception of Seasat data and by September 1, 1978, the station was in full operation. A little later in 1978 further modifications were made to allow the reception of data from the Tiros-N satellite which was launched in August of 1978; this satellite has four digital channels of visible and infrared data, and the station provides system-corrected images, computer compatible tapes and photo-and computer-fax of selected scenes in real time. Landsat and Tiros-N data are presently being supplied to the Canadian Coast Guard and to Ice Forecasting Central, Ottawa, on a routine basis via photofax transmissions direct from Shoe Cove.

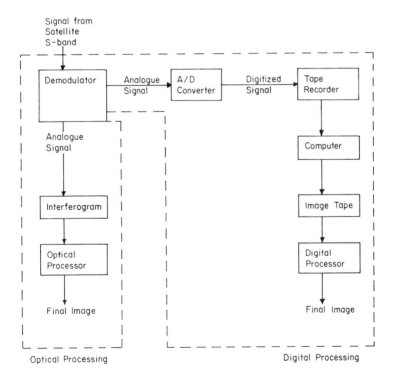

Figure 46. Reception and Processing of Seasat Data.

The reception and processing of signals from Seasat required a somewhat different installation of equipment. As mentioned in the last chapter, data from the altimeter, the scatterometer, the microwave radiometer and the visible and infrared radiometer were collected on a global basis and tape-recorded on board the satellite. They could subsequently be played back on request.

As far as results from the synthetic aperture radar system are concerned the satellite sent data to earth in analogue form at a wavelength in the S-band (about 10 cm). In order to find out the position on the ground to which the signal referred, it was necessary to know the Doppler frequency shift as outlined in Chapter III; this required recording not only the frequency spectrum of the returned signal but also the exact frequency of the coherent pulse which was sent to the ground in the first place. At the ground receiving station the equipment received both of these signals – the raw Doppler return and the coherent frequency reference –and compared them in the demodulator as shown in Figure 46. In other words this unit beat the coherent reference against the Doppler spectrum to give an analogue resultant. This signal was then passed to an A/D (analogue to digital) formatter and the digitized output went to a tape recorder, a computer and was finally recorded on a computer compatible tape. At this point the data could go through a series of mathematical computations to obtain an image. Alternatively instead of going the digital route it was possible to optically process the analogue data from the demodulator. In this case the first step would be to record a film representing the resultant of the two original signals (i.e. the Doppler return and the transmitted pulse). This film would be analogous to a hologram or interferogram in the visible part of the spectrum. Then using a laser beam, which is also coherent, this interferogram or signal film could be converted to an image of the scene (the image film). We thus have two routes – the digital and the optical. There is a formidable amount of data involved and of the two methods the digital is the better; it gives more detail and when all the necessary corrections are made it is more accurate. However it takes a long time to process. Present research is directed towards shortening this time.

Information on Seasat scenes available may also be obtained from User Assistance and Marketing Unit.

A process has been developed for the reception of microwave systems in aircraft which will display a scene almost immediately, as described in Chapter IV. However these quick look images do not have the quality of the digitally processed scenes from Seasat.

CHAPTER VI

FROM DATA TO INFORMATION

So we now have in our hands a tremendous amount of data about earth scenes all recorded digitally on computer tapes. We have seen how some simple corrections can be applied before preliminary processing, but there is far more to it than that. A number of different techniques have been devised to enable more valid interpretations to be obtained for special purposes. Pictorial presentation has its merits; we are used to judging situations with our eyes and a visual scene has more impact; eyeball interpretation is quick and easily understandable. However for quantitative assessments we must use numbers, and corrections, either radiometric or geometric, must be made mathematically. Fortunately since the data is already in digital form it is an easy matter to apply computer methods. We will consider both optical and digital* processing in this chapter.

Let us look first of all at how the images are produced. Whether the original data came from RBV or MSS sensors, it can now be presented pictorially directly from the tapes by means of an electron beam image recorder. An electron beam image recorder is something like the picture tube of your T.V. set. In both, an electron beam modulated by incoming signals sweeps across a screen to produce a picture. With a T.V. tube we view the picture directly on a screen; with the electron beam image recorder the screen is replaced by photographic film. The result is a black and white transparency just like one you can get from any

---

* For those interested in the basic principles of digital methods, a good report has been issued by the Canada Centre for Remote Sensing entitled "Introduction to Digital Images and Digital Analysis Techniques". This is really a self-teaching exercise to be carried out by the reader, designed to lead to a better understanding of the manipulation of digital data.

camera except that it is of higher quality. Photographic film is more sensitive to an electron beam than it is to a light beam, and so a slower, less grainy film can be used resulting in better resolution. We would expect this process to give a negative transparency. A bright light as viewed by the satellite would give rise to a strong signal which, after transmission to the ground and taping, would be transferred to the electron beam and give rise to a dark spot on the film. Normally this would be so, but by means of a little electronic gadgetry the process can be reversed so that we get at this stage a positive transparency. We generally like to see things this way, but, if a negative transparency is wanted, we can have this too. It just depends on what it is eventually wanted for. In this way we can obtain a 70 mm transparency; this may be repeated for each of the four spectral bands of the MSS data. From these can be made prints and enlargements of almost any size. The sizes which are supplied as standard vary from 70 mm up to 1.2 metres square. They may be supplied as positive or negative transparencies, or as positive prints. They may also be supplied as colour composites.

The question now is what do we want, black and white or colour? Many experienced interpreters prefer black and white transparencies. The resolution is better and for close detail this will be the prime consideration. However, for the rest of us colour has certain advantages, as we are able to distinguish boundaries better between different colours than between different shades of grey; also the colours themselves give us another piece of information.

To produce a colour composite we use as a starting point the 70 mm black and white transparencies from the electron beam image recorder of any three of the four spectral bands. They are then put in a sophisticated type of composite printer/enlarger, where any three of the transparencies (say bands 4, 5 and 6 from the MSS) are exposed individually to a different coloured light - blue, green or red - and these exposures are all superimposed on an ordinary colour film. You can see in the case of the MSS that by choosing three transparencies, either negative or positive, from four spectral bands, and in turn exposing each of these to any of three coloured lights, a very large number of colour combinations is possible. In practice it is found that most requirements are met by generating two combinations, Colour-1 and Colour-2. Colour-1 is an approximation of colour-infrared photographic film and is made by superimposing the green band transparency exposed with blue light, the red band transparency exposed with green light and one of the infrared bands (700 to 800 nm) exposed with red light. This colour would be the choice for anyone wishing to identify vegetation. Alternatively, Colour-2 may give more valuable information for other purposes. Here the master transparencies of both infrared bands are used as well as the visible red, and the colours of the lights are reversed. The red band transparency is exposed with red light, the nearest infrared band (700 to 800 nm) transparency is exposed with green light, and the second infrared band transparency (800 to 1,100 nm) with blue light. This might be the choice for anyone wishing to identify lakes and rivers. As all of this may seem a bit confusing, let us try to clarify things by making a table of them.

MSS Transparency Band			
Green 500 nm to 600 nm	Red 600 nm to 700 nm	Infrared 700 nm to 800 nm	Infrared 800 nm to 1,100 nm
Colour-1 Light of Exposure			
Blue	Green	Red	----
Colour-2 Light of Exposure			
----	Red	Green	Blue

These colour composites can give some very striking and dramatic effects and are a considerable aid in interpreting the photographs, once you get over the shock of seeing, perhaps, black rivers wending their way between red fields, or some such colour combination. After all, the colours are not just to make the pictures look pretty. They are selected to show up the required features more easily. Plates (III & IV) are examples of such colour composites.

Looking at any of these photographic-type images gives us a great deal of information. Photographs have long been familiar to us and, despite the fact that the colours may seem strange, we can easily comprehend the pictures and relate what we see on them to the features on the ground. However, there is far more data on the tapes than can be portrayed in this type of image. The data on the tapes is raw data telemetered directly from the satellite and has not been subjected to any of the deterioration that is inevitable in any intermediate image-producing process. In photographic reproduction we are limited by the physical shortcomings, both optical and spatial, of the film or printing paper. Printing paper is capable of giving us only about 14 discernible shades of grey, whereas the satellite data is transmitted in the form of digits having values from 0 to 63. At this point we have reduced our optical resolution by a factor of a little more than 4. Spatially the loss is even more serious. You remember that the multispectral scanner in Landsat sweeps the terrain across a swath 185 km wide, each sweep is afterwards divided optically into six bands each 79 m in width. As it traverses the swath it takes 3240 readings from one side to the other. In the direction of flight a distance of 185 km will contain 2340 of such bands, thus giving about 7 1/2 million data elements for a 185 km square piece of ground.

These are recorded on the MSS tape for each of the 4 spectral bands, giving a total of 31 million readings. It is impossible to re-create this detail on 4 films 70 mm square. Each of these small data elements, a pixel, corresponds to an area on the earth of 57 metres by 79 metres. At a scale of 1,000,000 to 1, each pixel would be represented on the picture by an area 5.7×10^{-3} cm x 7.9×10^{-3} cm, which would be quite impossible to be seen. Figure 47 shows the size of the swath and a pixel on the ground.

These are some of the problems we have to contend with in the area of spatial resolution when we try to represent satellite data on a standard image. Only with the aid of high-speed digital computers can we make use of all the data sent to us by the satellite. Taking the data directly from computer compatible tapes enables us to make use of each of these over 7,000,000 items of data individually, or the computer can average the readings from any given number of pixels depending on the detail required. For example, averaging over a block 10 pixels wide and 10 pixels long would still give over 70,000 individual readings for a ground area 185 km x 185 km. The results can be fed into mathematical models and combined with other data without any attempt being made to represent them pictorially. Data from weather satellites, which is of an ephemeral nature, can be combined with numerical data from other sources to arrive quickly at a complete forecast.

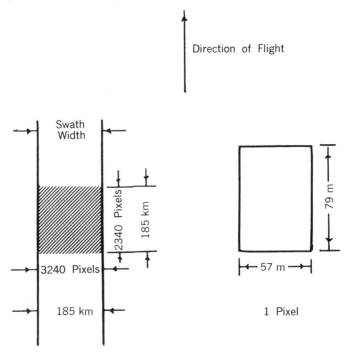

Figure 47. Ground Coverage of a Single Scene and of a Single Pixel.

Small areas of a scene can be selected for pictorial representation and studied in detail. An example of this is the study of the flow of water and sedimentation around Point Pelee in Lake Erie which is discussed further in Chapter VIII. Figures 55 and 56 show the pictorial representation of a small portion of this map obtained from data taken directly from the computer compatible tapes. In this case the total energy of reflected light from each pixel was used by the computer to print out a map automatically.

The example just considered represents a relatively simple type of computer mapping; it gives a black and white reproduction with good detail. Other more sophisticated types of computers may be used for classifying materials and ground details on the basis of their spectral signatures. Before discussing the image classifier in detail we will give a little more consideration to the correction of errors already in the records.

We must remember that remote sensing of the earth by satellite has been carried out on a regular basis for less than 10 years. During that time great strides have been made in developing methods for the correction and enhancement of imagery. At first only the simplest and most obvious of errors were removed; later more sophisticated types of equipment led to higher accuracy and improved interpretation. Since at that time Landsat was the only satellite in existence designed specifically for observation of the earth, it stood to reason that these methods were based on Landsat data obtained from the multispectral scanner. Now we have other satellites appearing with different orbits and different sensors, and their images are covering different areas of the earth. We want to be able to compare their respective images, perhaps to take some data from one satellite and some from another, or even from an aircraft. In other words we want to process the original data so that we end up with an image having a format which is independent of the satellite or other platform which produced it.

The importance of this platform-independence cannot be overstressed. Several countries such as France, Japan, the European Space Agency and others will soon have their own remote sensing satellites in space, and they will each have their own package of sensors which will probably be similar to though not quite the same as, those of Landsat. The multiplicity of images will lead to a chaotic situation unless some means of converting them to a common format exists.

To meet this situation C.C.R.S. has developed a new device, called the *Digital Image Correction System* (DICS). This system not only converts the data to a common format but automatically carries out a number of radiometric and geometric corrections to yield an extremely accurate product. It produces a geocoded image which can be readily combined with data available from Canadian geographic information systems.

The heart of the DICS is a mini-computer which takes uncorrected image data recorded on computer compatible tapes at either Prince Albert or Shoe Cove, converts the data to Universal Transverse Mercator (UTM) coordinates, checks them with known ground control points and resamples the original values. The result is a very accurate, high-precision computer compatible tape fully corrected for radiometric and geometric errors and compatible with NTS data. It covers an area one quarter that of a 1:250,000 NTS map (0.5° latitude by 1.0° longitude) and is able to give an image of an entire Landsat scene to an accuracy of 30 m. This accuracy is quite remarkable when we consider that the data is received from a satellite 900 km above us, which is subject to pitch, yaw and minor variations in height and velocity.

It is understandable that the correction of an image to such a degree of accuracy takes time. The use of DICS would not always be justified for day to day production of every Landsat image, but it does have particular value for, say, the location of islands and for other geographical features as will be discussed further in Chapter VII. It is also useful when we are wanting to add together data from images received at different times (i.e. multitemporal imagery), and in change detection techniques. Although we have here been talking about the application of DICS to Landsat it may, in fact, be applied to any sort of imagery, either airborne or spaceborne.

This leads to some interesting possibilities. For example, we saw that radar methods give very high spatial resolution, while multispectral scanner imagery gives good spectral resolution. What could we expect in the way of extra information by combining the two?

The idea of combining airborne SAR data with Landsat multispectral data was tried out in the summer of 1978 by scientists at C.C.R.S., who used this method to gather information on potato crops on an agricultural site located near Grand Falls, New Brunswick. In order to obtain good registration between the two scenes, Landsat imagery was corrected on the DICS equipemnt. SAR data was also corrected and both were overlaid on a common grid of UTM coordinates. These preliminary experiments gave some promising results and suggested that further work along these lines would be well worthwhile.

The combination of Seasat SAR data with Landsat multispectral scanner data has been tried out in the laboratories of MacDonald, Dettwiler and Associates, resulting in a very dramatic MSS/SAR colour composite as shown in Plate X. In order to acquire good registration both Landsat and Seasat images were rectified to UTM coordinates. Using a precision rectified Landsat image as the reference the Seasat image was brought into registration with that of the Landsat image to give perfect alignment. The intensity of the black and white Seasat image was then used to modulate the coloured Landsat image from bands 4, 5 and 6. Referring to Plate IX we can see that the Seasat image, (1), taken on June 6, 1978, shows good detail; bridges over the river are clearly seen, and the image contains good surface texture and surface terrain characteristics typical of synthetic aperture radar. The Landsat image, (b), has inferior spatial resolution; details are not so clearly discernible, but it contains good information on surface reflectivity. By combining the two, Plate X, we can see the advantages of integrating the information into one image. The Landsat/Seasat image shows bridges, roads and other terrain quite clearly, whereas the structures are not so clear in the Landsat image. This technique has the advantage of being very flexible and may be modified to suit the needs of different classes of users - geologists, foresters, urban planners, etc., because different colour combinations can be used, and different areas in either image can be enhanced to any chosen degree.

This technique is an exciting new development in our compendium of image-making tricks. It is only in an early stage of development, but gives glimpses of great promise. Since all the steps are digitally manipulated by a computer, the production of such imagery can be carried out quite routinely on a suitable image analysis system. These methods also have an application to any future remote sensing satellite system combining MSS and SAR in the same satellite.

Having reduced all errors in our image whether from the

air or from space to an absolute minimum, we are ready to interpret it. However a preliminary study may show that it would be worthwhile to enhance the image, or at least the part of it that we are particularly interested in.

There are several ways of improving the interpretability of a scene which will allow the user to get yet a little more information from the original data. As already discussed in connection with density slicing described in Chapter III, one of the main areas where enhancement is sought is in the differentiation of varying shades of grey. We saw there how varying shades of grey on a film could be divided into distinct greyness ranges; these in turn could be displayed as a different colour. We also saw how in some scenes the actual greyness values may occupy only quite a small range; the very light values or the very dark values may be absent and the rest of the scene may not show much gradation. We want to increase the contrast. In order to make better use of the full scale of values (256 brightness levels) the instrument can give us, we can take this smaller range and stretch it to occupy the full scale. This is referred to as *linear stretch*; it has the effect of decreasing the low values and increasing the high values. This linear stretch may be applied to even smaller areas where differences in greyness levels are even smaller, and this range expanded again. A picture may have a predominantly light area and a predominantly dark area. It is possible to take each of these and stretch each independently to cover the full range of brightness values. Alternatively the whole image may be stretched over the range of values given by, say, the light area. This would then show up a great deal more detail here, but would mean that the darker part of the scene would all be black and detail would be lost. Conversely, if the image were to be stretched between the limiting values of the dark part, the lighter areas would all be white and show no detail while the dark parts in their turn would be enhanced.

Another form of enhancement is called *edge enhancement*. In this case the image as a whole is not stretched, but local differences between any individual pixel and its surroundings can be exaggerated. For example, if one pixel is only a little lighter than the average value of the surrounding pixels, this difference may be doubled, thus making it more recognizable.

These enhancements may be applied not only to black and white imagery but also to colour composites; by adjusting the range of values of the different spectral bands we can achieve a better spectral resolution. Colour differentiation can also be achieved by taking each pixel separately and expressing its value as a ratio of two bands, say band 4 to band 5 of the Landsat multispectral scanner. The main problem here is to know which two hands to choose; this is something which can only be learned by experience. By choosing the right band combination the colours may be enhanced to enable the interpreter to get a great deal more information out of the scene.

By now we have travelled a long way from the relatively simple imagery produced directly from the aircraft or satellite. The scenes have been radiometrically and geometrically corrected, and they have been enhanced. We are now ready to analyze them. This is done on an image classifier, or an image analysis system. Briefly, this is a computer which takes data from a digitized tape such as that from a Landsat satellite, analyzes it pixel by pixel, and classifies the objects on it according to their spectral signatures. It is not necessary for the computer to know what these spectral signatures represent; it merely recognizes that they are the same as, or different from, each other.

As a simple case, let us consider an image of a blue river flowing through green fields. We can first of all present the tape to the computer and ask it how many classes of material it can differentiate. It will reply by telling us that there are two classes of material here; that there is a cluster of pixels (the river) having the same spectral signature against a background having different characteristics (the fields). It can print out the course of the river by printing dots on paper, one for each pixel, or we can ask it to print R or some other symbol for all points with this same spectral signature.

We can also ask the computer to display the scene on a colour T.V. tube and, by pressing the appropriate buttons, we can choose the colours we would like to see it in. We can then, if we wish, take a coloured photograph of it for permanent record. Alternatively we can ask it to record the results on a digital tape which may later be used for producing an image with the electron beam image recorder as described earlier. The input to this operation is a computer tape which feeds scanner data into the computer; the output may be in the form of a printer map, a colour T.V. display which will give us a coloured photograph, or a digital tape. The original input tape may be from a satellite, or it can be digitized data from any photograph, such as from airborne photography, etc.

As we go to more complicated patterns the computer may reply to the original question as to how many different colours or spectral signatures it can differentiate by telling us it can separate 5 such materials, say, or some other number depending on the image analysis system used. This process of gathering together areas with the same spectral signature is known as *clustering*, and each class of material so classified is known as a *theme*. We can ask the computer to print out, or show us on the T.V. tube, a complete thematic map of all these clusters, each printed with a symbol indicating the class, or we can ask it to display the clusters on a T.V. tube each in a different colour.

At this stage we have merely sorted out the material into a number of different clusters. This is an *unsupervised* classification. We do not know what these clusters represent. That is the next stage. For this we require more information in order that we may train the computer to tell us what is there. We need ground truth data of a small part of the scene which may be provided by aerial survey, by existing forest cover maps or by farmers on the ground. We need to know that one small area is, in fact, corn, say, or spruce, or paved roads, or whatever theme we wish to portray. Knowing this we can then train the computer to go over the whole area and complete a thematic map. It means that if we know the characteristics of trees in a forest, for example, from information taken from the easily accessible areas on the edge, we can very quickly map the inaccessible areas in the depths of the forest. These methods have been used extensively for making forest inventories as will be seen later in Chapter IX. If we want to estimate the yield of an orchard such as an orange grove we can take multis-pectral aerial photographs of the grove, present them in digitized form to the computer and train it to recognize the spectral signature of an orange so that it will produce a thematic map of oranges; it will even calculate for us the percentage of the image area containing oranges, from which the farmer can estimate the total yield.

How do we train the computer to recognize and identify classes of material? Once again for the sake of simplicity we will take a 2-theme case. Perhaps we want to know the extent of marsh grass in a wetlands region, because its presence is an indication of the health of the area. We throw on to the screen an image of the area. From this we select a small portion known to be marsh grass and we outline this area with an electronic fence which we can draw on the screen this fence or cursor is easily operated with a joystick control, and its size, shape and position can be adjusted to fit over the sample area. We then say to the computer "This marsh grass. Go over the whole picture and map out for us all areas with the same spectral signature." We might also add "Tell us how much of the total area is occupied with marsh grass." We can ask it to print a letter M for each pixel having the same spectral signature as marsh grass, or we can ask it to display those areas on the screen in colour. This is called a *supervised* classification.

We have used a 2 theme classification as an example, but further levels of classfication could give us more themes depending on the classifier being used. An example of this may be seen in Plate V which represents a thematic map of the area around Port Mouton in Nova Scotia. The data was taken from digital tapes provided by Landsat-I when it passed over the area on May 3, 1974; the classification was carried out in connection with the Atlantic Coastal Resource Inventory. The inland areas were of no immediate concern and so were not classified; they appear black. The coastal areas, on the other hand, were classified in some detail as indicated by the accompanying colour code. The small inset shows a four times enlargement of the Summerville Beach area. This was one of the early studies of coastal areas and the aim was to see to what extent computer systems could be used for the purpose along the Atlantic Seaboard. Coastal areas present some special difficulties in that the sea and the adjoining land constitute a dynamic system; the tides create changes; parts of the coast are eroded while other parts experience a build-up of sand. The land behind it may be swamped with water at some times of the year, and the vegetation difficult to map. However the results showed that resource mapping from satellite is feasible along the coast, and these methods will probably be used for similar studies in maritime regions.

Another example of this classification procedure is given in Chapter IX, where a small portion of Plate III (as marked by a small square) was selected for study. Figure 61 shows an alphabetically coded thematic map of the area; Plates VI and VII show colour-enhanced diagrams of the same area. These will be discussed in greater detail in Chapter IX in the section relating to forestry.

It is obvious that displaying a scene pixel by pixel will give a considerable enlargement. Since it is not possible to represent the seven and a half million data elements of a Landsat photograph on a single computer print-out or on a T.V. screen, it must be done in a piecemeal fashion. The computer described could cope with an area only 512 pixels wide and 512 pixels high, or a total of 262, 144 pixels. This is approximately 1/30 of the area of the original picture. The speed with which it operates is amazing. Once the computer has been trained it can produce classified results in a matter of seconds. This has proved invaluable in the study of land use classification, and allows whole areas to be classified in a matter of hours which would previously have taken weeks.

We can make use of classification methods to show us how conditions may be changing over a period of time; for example the computer may be trained to recognize water or even moisture-laden soil, and to block these patterns out pixel by pixel over areas prone to flooding; if this is done for successive passes of the satellite over a period of time, valuable information can be gained by noting differences in the images. A technique known as *Change Detection* enables these changes to be recognized without the visual image actually being created. Records of the same area from different passes of the satellite may be compared automatically, and only differences between the two will be presented. This will mean a great saving in time as it will reduce the amount of data that has to be examined.

The procedure just described was carried out at C.C.R.S. by the Image-100 and is the basis for other image analyzers.

The increasing demand for image classification and analysis has led to the development of a number of systems of varying degrees of complexity and, of course, at varying costs. The cheaper instruments are not generally inferior to the more expensive models as far as accuracy goes, but they are for the most part slower in operation and they do not have the same flexibility. However they do allow the user to get into the field at a not too prohibitive cost. Most of the instruments are modular in construction and may be added to as the situation becomes more demanding, or the interpreter more experienced.

The Canada Centre for Remote Sensing has modified the Image-100 and added to it another sub-system to make the whole an extremely sophisticated piece of equipment. The improved system is known as the C.C.R.S. Image Analysis System and is referred to as C.I.A.S. The corrections and enhancements described above are carried out within the analyzer itself, which is able to accept computer compatible tapes, maps or aerial photographs. The system will handle a considerably higher work load than its predecessor. It enables us to classify, for example, a full Landsat image (i.e. 7,000,000 pixels in 4 colour bands) potentially into 93 classes in less than 14 minutes. This is a tremendous amount of data to be handled in such a short time. The process would be carried out in several stages. For example, there might first be a simple breakdown into water and land masses. The water areas might then be studied further and classified into 6 or 7 areas with different spectral signatures. The land scenes might be classified generally into agricultural, urban or forestry areas, and all of these could again be taken individually and classified more minutely. The results are presented in the form of single class plots scaled to approximately match map scales from 1:50,000 to 1:1,000,000, colour photographs, computer tapes and tabular listings of statistical results, such as class acreages, etc. This obviously is a great step forward in the development of image interpretation, and since the system is placed at the disposal of the remote sensing community, it should be of great benefit to a number of researchers.

The Ontario Centre for Remote Sensing employs an image analysis system consisting of two terminals for interaction with a computer and two image display units.

This system corrects the geometry of LANDSAT images to match the Universal Transverse Mercator grid, before classification of the data is performed. After the image data has been classified and a tape of the results produced, a computerized colour plotting system automatically produces a colour map. The plotter is capable of providing up to 256 shades of colour (although OCRS programs have to date used only 32), and prints them on a sheet of ordinary paper measuring 56 cm by 86 cm. At the present time, maps can be produced at any selected scale with a UTM grid, longitude and latitude references, legend, delineation of theme boundaries in black and white, and annotation of features by characters or graphic sysmbols. In addition, programs have been written to permit users of the system to effect outlining, shading and annotation of features by controlling a cursor on the image display monitor. Other programs permit the combination of imagery from more than one season within a single map, in order to achieve more accurate results and to enable comparisons between different years to be made.

Development is not only active in government circles but in industry as well. Nearly all the image analysis systems being produced are capable of carrying out radiometric corrections and some degree of image enhancement as a processing stage before classification.

Dipix Systems Ltd. of Ottawa worked in cooperation with the Canada Centre for Remote Sensing in some phases of the design of the C.I.A.S. described above. They have themselves developed a range of systems from a simple system at a cost of a few thousand dollars up to a very elaborate model costing about a million dollars. MacDonald, Dettwiler and Associates of Vancouver produce a medium-cost instrument, and others have been designed for special purposes by OVAAC-8 of Toronto. In general, systems can be designed to suit the purpose and the price range the customer desires. As mentioned above many of these are of modular construction; a simple system may be purchased in the first place and added to later as experience dictates.

With such instruments as these at our disposal the art of interpretation is progressing rapidly, and the situation is not static; all of these companies are even now working on further improvements and are willing to cooperate on special designs to suit special purposes.

An interesting sideline to the development of classifiers is the application to problems entirely outside the realm of remote sensing for which they were originally designed. They can be used on any photographic-type imagery - for example, that relating to military systems, brain-scanning equipment, X-ray pictures, etc., and there is promise of application to other biological problems. A number of such techniques are at present being developed in our Universities and show how the spin-off of ideas from one area of technology can enrich another.

CHAPTER VII

THE LAND WE LIVE ON

In general, remote sensing methods allow us to describe the earth, and that of course is the essence of geography. Aerial photography is by now a well-established technique, and the development of new sensors is revolutionizing airborne imagery. In spite of these modern techniques, however, mapping from the air is expensive and time-consuming. Within the time-span of even a single flight, weather conditions may change considerably and the sun angle will vary. The result is that we do not have nearly as many maps as we would like. A lot still remains to be done. Not only do we want to complete the map-making on a larger scale, but all the old maps have to be constantly revised to keep them up-to-date. Coast lines change with time; construction projects such as dams and hydro-electric schemes change the face of the land; rivers are diverted, and new highways are built; there is an ever-continuing expansion of our cities into the surrounding countryside. The task of the map-maker is monumental, and the cost of doing all we should like to do would be prohibitive by existing methods. Let us look then at the help we can get from satellites.

Generally speaking, the information from satellites is limited to small-scale mapping. But before brushing this aside as being of little importance, let us see just how much we can do working within this limitation. For some purposes the small-scale synoptic view has definite advantages. It is possible to see gross geographical features such as fault lines, folds, and geographical lineaments much better on a small-scale map, and many new ones have in fact been discovered recently by use of Landsat imagery. Regional patterns - either physiographic or cultural - are easily distinguished. They show up particularly well in the winter when there is snow on the ground and the sun angle, being low, casts more pronounced shadows. An example of winter imagery may be seen in Figure 48 (C.C.R.S. Ref. No. 10888-

14502). This is a Landsat photograph taken over Lake Manicouagan on December 28, 1974; we can see how the accumulation of snow on the frozen lake and in the crevices of the surrounding rock enhances the structural features. The lake was formed in a crater made by the impact of a large meteorite falling many millions of years ago. The centre was later pushed up by pressures below to give a ring-shaped depression about 59 miles in diameter. Lake Manicouagan now serves as a major water reservoir for northeastern Quebec.

Satellite imagery allows such photographs to be obtained quickly, cheaply and effectively. If aircraft were used, it would be necessary to take a large number of photographs and to make a mosaic of them. These photographs would have to be taken at different times of the day under different lighting conditions. Landsat is able to provide us with an almost instantaneous image of an area 185 km square and in a few minutes it can cover a swath of land 185 km across from North to South of Canada. The lighting conditions over this brief period of time would probably be uniform.

It is sometimes argued that the positional accuracy of Landsat is not sufficiently good to allow accurate location on a map. However, recently developed techniques, such as the digital image correction system discussed in Chapter VI, have shown a great improvement over earlier methods of error correction. It must be stressed that no form of remote sensing from either airborne or space sensors provides accurate location without the prior definition of a number of ground control points, which can serve as reference points. In Canada, however, there are large inaccessible areas of the country where ground control points are sparse and not always of the accuracy we would like.

There have been occasions where the smaller scale of Landsat images has allowed geographic features to be located more accurately than could be done by aircraft. The exact location of roads and other features is sometimes difficult in remote areas where there are few details of terrain to serve as landmarks. Photographs from aircraft cover such a small area that there may be no other details on them to which a road position may be related. To take an actual example, the road to Tungsten in the Yukon had

The Land We Live On

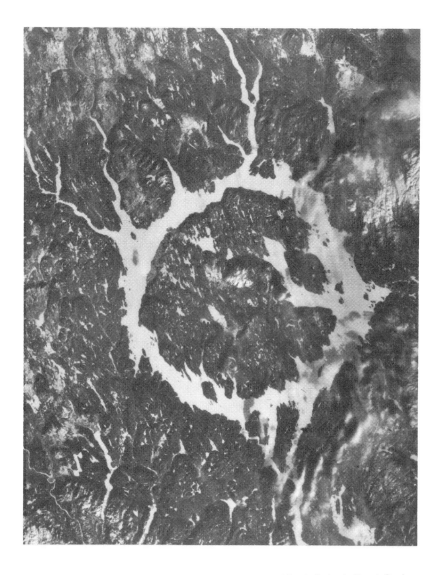

Courtesy of Canada Centre for Remote Sensing

Figure 48. Landsat Image of Lake Manicouagan.

been surveyed from the air and had been approximately located on a published map of scale 1:250,000, but was found from Landsat photographs to be in error by 1500 m for one part of its length. The large scale aerial photographs were re-examined and it was seen that in this particular section there was very little mapped detail. The same thing applies to other linear features in remote areas such as rivers, power lines, pipe lines and aquaducts.

A very useful application for Landsat imagery is the up-dating of maps. As in the example quoted above, satellite photography has shown that occasionally rivers, highways, coastlines and islands have been inadequately located. This applies particularly in remote areas such as the Arctic, and this is the very area where at the moment we are most in need of accurate information. The Arctic area is tremendously rich in resources and is expected to undergo phenomenal development within the next twenty-five years. The whole area is pregnant with the most exciting possibilities, and Canada has to be ready for this development; otherwise some other country will be. The need for revision of the existing 1:250,000 scale series of maps and for new 1:50,000 scale coverage is becoming increasingly evident in northern areas. Safe air and sea navigation require the accurate positioning of myriads of small off-shore islands. When no ground control points exist, the cost of establishing them on these islands could be prohibitive. Conventional aerial photography cannot usually bridge the water gaps between islands, but the approximately 35,000 square kilometre coverage of a Landsat image usually bridges the gaps quite easily.

An example of this was the production of new 1:50,000 maps of the Dubawnt Lake area in the Northwest Territories. The lake itself is approximately 100 km long and 60 km wide and contains 10 islands. For the new maps the position of these islands had to be verified. There was such a large distance of water between each that normal aerial photography could not be used as there would have been an insufficient number of land points to link the pictures together. By using Landsat images in conjunction with the CCRS Digital Image Correction System it was proved possible to position the islands with an accuracy comparable with the compilation standards set for these sheets. The system is capable of providing correction throughout an entire Landsat image to an accuracy of about 30 m on average. Had the location of the islands been derived from the current 1:250,000 mapping, position errors of up to 250 m would have been carried over into the 1:50,000 mapping.

In 1976 the Atlantic Hydrographic Services set out to survey the Labrador coast. The nothwestern part of the coast is particularly hazardous with narrow fiords, high mountain ranges close to the shore and numerous unsurveyed small islands and rocks scattered up to a distance of 16 km from the coast. These were obviously highly dangerous to shipping in an area which was fast developing. It would not have been practicable to survey the whole of the area in detail by ship because of the time and cost involved, but by a preliminary study of Landsat data it was possible to cut down this time to such an extent that the whole project became feasible. Three Landsat images were used from three different orbits on three different dates. At this latitude there was a fair amount of overlap of scenes, and so two or more independent positions could be determined for some of the shoals. Figure 49 shows the way the Landsat images were positioned over the territory. Control points are shown as Δ , and offshore features as O .

Provided with this preliminary data from Topographical Survey, a ship, C.C.S. Baffin, and helicopter parties were able to go in and verify the existence and position of these shoals. Many of them had previously been uncharted, among them eight rocks and an island, subsequently named Landsat Island. It presented the most easterly feature off the coast at this point and was the largest of several uncharted rocks, being aprroximately 25 m long, 45 m wide and about 6 m high. When the helicopter crew went in later to verify its position the sole occupant was a polar bear. The crew decided not to land.

We can see that by means of satellite imagery several features previously uncharted were detected. Conversely a check was made on the presence of three reported off-shore islands which did not appear on Landsat images. These were found, in fact, not to exist. Soundings carried out by launch and positioned by radar-ranging from C.C.S. Baffin showed minimum depths in these areas to be 160 m, 42 m and

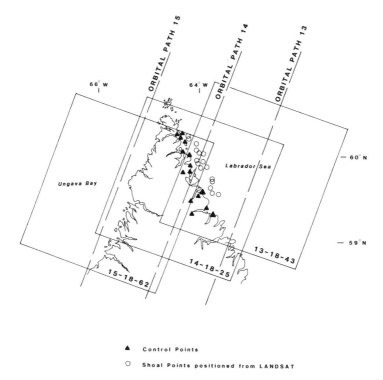

▲   Control Points

O   Shoal Points positioned from LANDSAT

Courtesy of Topograpical Survey of Canada and Canadian Hydrographic Service.

Figure 49. Landsat Coverage of the Northwestern Labrador Coast.

18.9 m respectively. So it would seem that either these "islands" had been erroneously reported or had since disappeared.

This operation showed how useful Landsat imagery can be for preliminary studies, saving the time and money for subsequent surveys.

In 1975 the National Air Photo Library produced a complete set of Landsat mosaics covering the whole of Canada at a scale of 1:1,000,000. The coverage in black and white required over 1000 Landsat scenes. Colour mosaics are now also available for all the Provinces and some of the Arctic areas. They are obtainable from the National Air Photo Library in Ottawa.

For cartographic applications black and white records are generally preferred because of the better definition.

For the study of other earth features composite colour imagery is able to give further information. We will use as an example a Landsat picture of the Montreal area taken on September 3rd, 1972 (Plate III). As mentioned in the foreword, it is unfortunate that the detail of imagery reproduced in a book inevitably suffers a certain degradation in processing, partly because of the reduction of scale and partly because of the difficulty of exact colour reproduction. If you would like to see an original 9 inch by 9 inch copy of this image it can be obtained from CCRS, Ottawa, Canada quoting the reference number E-1004-15170-5. The picture shows the country around the Montreal area extending from Ottawa in the West to the Richelieu River in the East, from Cornwall and the Adirondacks in the South to the Maskinonge River in the North. It was a day fairly free from cloud although a few white puffs can be discerned scattered across the scene particularly in the northeast quarter of the picture along the St. Lawrence River. The image was obtained using bands 4, 5 and 6 covering the wavelength ranges 500–600 nanometres (green), 600–700 nanometres (red), and 700–800 nanometres (near infrared). If the black and white transparencies from these bands are exposed with blue, green and red light respectively, we obtain a false-colour image type C1. Here water, being very absorbent in the near infrared, shows up black when it is deep and light blue in shallow areas where it has particles in suspension; vegetation, being strongly reflective in the infrared, shows up as red; the forests with their almost continuous canopy of leaves show dark red, while the fields are a little lighter. Built-up areas and roads show up lighter and rather greyish in colour.

At first sight a picture such as this appears somewhat confusing, but an expert interpreter can get a lot of information from it. The key opposite the plate outlines some of the features depicted. If you wish to interpret the coloured image in detail, you may like to trace this diagram in ink on a sheet of plastic and place it over the Landsat picture to make an overlay. The following page gives the key to the symbols used. You may be surprised then at the details portrayed. You will notice that the boundary between the darker tones of the Boreal forest region (Missinaibi-Cabonga section) and the lighter tones of the St.

Lawrence mixed forests is easily distinguished. On Mt. Tremblant, a little north of the Rouge River, it is interesting to note the change of colour going up the mountain slope. At the bottom it is reddish in colour denoting the presence of deciduous trees; at higher altitudes it becomes more greenish in colour as the deciduous give way to coniferous trees. Roads, even those under construction, show up clearly, as do the cities, towns and quite small settlements. Rivers and lakes are clearly defined, and here also we can see some evidence of turbid areas of the river at Baie de la Pentcote (T3) and in the estuarine delta of the St. Lawrence (T5). Other features will be evident from a study using the overlay and the key. This picture shows the great advantage of Landsat imagery for the location of linear geological structures such as faults and folds. The fold structures in the Grenville area show up particularly well.

If you are ordering a Landsat image of this scene, you may also like to order another of the same area obtained on October 11th, 1973 (E-10440-15155-3). It is interesting to compare them. The colours appear quite different. For one thing the bands used are 4, 5 and 7 instead of 4, 5 and 6 for the earlier one, and again in October leaves of the deciduous trees are less vigorous; they are either dying or the trees have shed their leaves altogether. This means there is a lower proportion of infrared light reflected and the whole picture has a more yellowish appearance. However, as you can see, the structural features of the land show up very much better.

You may say, "It is all very well interpreting an image when you already have ground information and know what is there, but it would be a different problem on unknown terrain." This is true, but it is only by studying the appearance of known features that we can obtain the expertise to deal with the unknown. Interpretation is not easy, but our interpreters are becoming increasingly skilled in this operation and have the special knowledge of their own disciplines behind them. This specialized expertise will probably always be necessary; it will require a forester with his knowledge of forestry to get the most out of a picture depicting forests; it will require a geographer with his knowledge of terrain to get the most out of a picture such as we have here.

Useful as visible-range satellite imagery may be for most parts of the world, it is useless for mapping areas enveloped in cloud and haze. In humid, tropical regions, particularly over jungle areas, bad visibility renders conventional photography inadequate, and here is where radar methods come into their own. This was demonstrated very dramatically in Darien Province, Panama. Over a period of 40 years of aerial photography it had been possible to map only a very small portion of the country, about 16,000 square kilometres in extent. A commercial company brought in a Caravelle aircraft fitted with a side-looking radar system (SLAR), and a complete set of maps was produced within about 6 hours, showing vegetation, drainage, streams, and so on. These results were so spectacular that the governments of Brazil, Venezuela and other tropical countries quickly followed suit. The mapping of the Amazon was again a triumph for radar, since it was the only method that would allow the penetration of the humid and cloudy atmospheres over the jungles; microwaves in the longer wavelength range can penetrate the canopy of leaves and vegetation to obtain information on the land and water beneath. New Guinea was mapped very successfully with radar, showing topographic features such as peaks shrouded in mists rising 5,000 metres above sea level. The radar imagery thus obtained provided the only maps available to field geologists seeking their way by plane or helicopter over this dangerous, hitherto unmapped terrain.

These repeated success stories led to a great surge of interest in radar methods until to-day practically all the tropical regions have been mapped. As the newer synthetic aperture systems with their higher resolution come into use, the work will no doubt be repeated from time to time to keep these maps up-to-date and to acquire more detail, but the importance of the early experiments in the history of remote sensing cannot be overestimated. They provided the only possible means of studying these impenetrable areas.

The same remarks also apply to the Arctic regions, especially in the winter when the days are so short or, in fact, to any coastal areas particularly in the North. Radar is again the most effective system for reconnaissance work and for routine surveillance. Figure 50 shows an example of

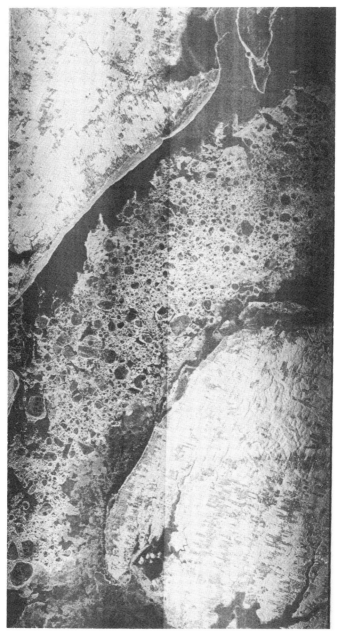

Courtesy of Dept. of National Defence, Goodyear Corp.   GEMS System, and Communications Research Centre.

Figure 50. Radar Image of Prince Edward Island and Nova Scotia.

imagery obtained with a synthetic aperture GMS radar
system flown in March 1974 at a height of 9,000 m. The two
strips totalling five miles in width represent two passes of
the aircraft and depict the southeastern tip of Prince
Edward Island, the Northumberland Strait and the Pictou
area of the Nova Scotia mainland. The wavelength used was
3 cm giving a resolution of about 15 m. It was a cloud-
covered day when conventional photography would not have
been possible; yet with radar good detail was given and we
can see the ice-floes in the Straits with open water showing
black along the shores. The inlets also held ice, but this ice
had a smooth surface as compared with the more broken
surface of the ice outside and so also appears black. At this
wavelength it is therefore difficult to distinguish between
shore-fast ice and open water. Despite the fact that both
ice and land areas were covered with snow, microwaves
were able to penetrate this to reveal with good clarity the
solid edge of the ice and the surface features of the land.

It was the success of experiments such as this that led to
the adoption of microwave methods in the Satellite Seasat.
It was unfortunate that its life was so short, but the results
obtained during that short time fully justified the hopes of
those who promoted the development of radar systems in
space. From orbits of approximately the same height, the
resolution obtainable using digital methods of image presentation is much greater in the case of Seasat than in the
case of Landsat. The picture shown in Figure 51 of Trois
Rivières, Québec, is the first digitally produced scene in the
world to have been recorded from Seasat. It covers an area
of 41 km by 38 km along the river and shows how much
detail can be derived. It was achieved by means of
computer tapes recorded at Shoe Cove and was processed in
the Vancouver laboratories of MacDonald, Dettwiler and
Associates Ltd.

The interpretation of a new type of scene is always
difficult until a fair amount of experience has been gained,
but one of the prominent features of this picture is the
detail shown of small streams and other linear
characteristics. Some of the streams are visible because
their banks are perpendicular to the radar beam and so send
reflections back to the receiver. The water itself,
particularly in the St. Lawrence, shows how sensitive radar

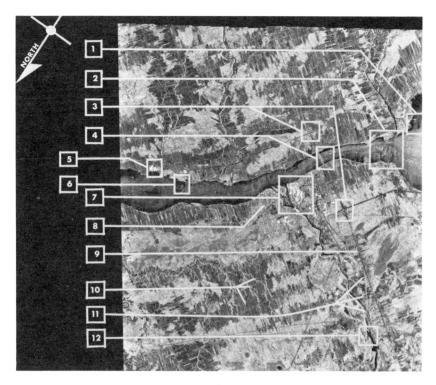

A Few Features Visible on the Trois Rivières Seasat Scene

1. Evidence of atmospheric phenomenon. (wind N.E. 6-8 knots)
2. Internal wave phenomenon probably caused by interaction between the flow of the St. Lawrence River leaving Lac St. Pierre and the small river entering from the south.
3. Highway interchanges.
4. Bridge with ships in the river. Note the inverted catenary support on the bridge superstructure, the reflection from the bridge deck off the water, and the wake from the ship closest to the bridge running under the bridge.
5. Gentilly Nuclear Power Station.
6. Marina. Note wind shadow from breakwater.
7. Trois Rivières.
8. Town of Cap de la Madeleine. Note the streets.
9. Divided highway. The median strip is visible.
10. CPR tracks.
11. CPR tracks with power transmission towers alongside.
12. Dam with reservoir.

Courtesy of MacDonald, Dettwiler and Associates, Ltd.

Figure 51. Seasat Image of Trois Rivières, Québec.

methods are to surface texture; smooth water appears dark, whereas rough water appears light. Rural and agricultural areas may be distinguished, the forested areas being brighter than the fields. The bridge over the river is very clear and displays some detail of structure, and several ships are visible. The industrial area of the city and the Gentilly nuclear power station are easily differentiated.

A somewhat different kind of cartography is the production of land-use maps. It is easy to see that satellite pictures have a ready application to synoptic mapping of large regions, but their usefulness is somewhat limited for small areas the size of cities. However, the methods of reproducing pictures direct from computer tapes are undergoing rapid development; density slicing techniques and computer printouts are evolving which contribute greatly to the enhancement of the images, and it is now possible to get very useful information from them for land-use studies. It takes a long time to collect the information and prepare a land-use map by conventional aerial photography, so that often by the time it is published it is already out-of-date. The preparation of maps from satellite data is much quicker; we therefore have to trade one advantage against another, and sometimes we would rather have an up-to-date map even though it does not show quite so much detail. In the U.S. land-use has been classified and mapped successfully by a number of investigators. An 11-category land-use map of the entire state of Rhode Island was produced in only eight man-days.

Although it is not generally possible to recognize city streets and individual blocks of buildings from Landsat maps, it is possible to identify highways crossing the countryside as may be seen in the image of the Montreal area map in Plate III. It is also possible to monitor the boundaries of cities and the degree to which urban sprawl is stretching out into the countryside. With the demand for more housing, communities are changing their zoning laws. The conversion that is now taking place of farm land to urban areas is of great concern to those who are looking ahead to the feeding of an expanding population. Change detection techniques are a great help in identifying such processes.

Planning to make the best use of the land and its

resources outside the cities can be helped by taking advantage of all types of remote sensing from the air and from space - black and white photography, multispectral systems, thermal infrared scanning and also radar. An example of a radar image is shown in Figure 52. It represents an urban area, Kanata, not far from Ottawa, and was obtained on August 1, 1978, by Intertech Remote Sensing Ltd., using synthetic aperture radar mounted on the Convair aircraft from Canada Centre for Remote Sensing. The amount of detail is impressive, and the resolution of about 3 metres allows even cars to be seen on the highway and individual houses on city streets. You may say "But, I have looked at just as good a picture from an ordinary aerial photograph". The advantage of radar imagery is that it can be taken any time, day or night in any kind of weather. Also, with synthetic aperture radar, resolution is independent of range; we are therefore able to choose the altitude and coverage we want without having to sacrifice detail.

Remote sensing methods are particularly valuable for the developing countries, where frequently land-use maps do not exist. An interesting example of this was a recent project carried out in Indonesia. The ultimate aim was a more effective utilization of the land and its many resources and a rapid development of its economy. Most of the existing maps were out of date, and information was lacking on the type and location of the country's natural resources and land use patterns. As with many eastern countries, the availability of rice is a critical factor if the population is to be adequately fed. Indonesia produces two classes of rice - one from fields which are permanently irrigated, and the other from fields which are irrigated only in the rainy season. The yield of the first is predictable; the yield from the second fluctuates from one season to another depending on the quantity and timeliness of the rain. It is therefore the yield from the second type of crop which determines whether or not there will be feast or famine, and so these areas were studied closely and their extent estimated. It was first planned to acquire accurate thematic maps of selected areas at a scale of 1:250,000, which would be extended eventually to the whole of the country. This was done from Landsat imagery and

Courtesy of SURSAT Project and Intertech Remote Sensing Ltd.

Figure 52. SAR Aircraft Image of Kanata, Ontario.

supplemented by airborne radar. The classification of land use was carried out using computer tapes. Two scenes of Lombok Island were chosen – one recorded on October 12, 1972 (dry season) and the other on June 21, 1973 (end of the rainy season). One of the difficulties in interpretation was the lack of local instrumentation such as image analyzers, etc. A preliminary unsupervised classification was carried out by NAC Incorporated in Tokyo and this showed that 9 different classes could be recognized, which were later identified by field tests as primary forest (dark green), secondary forest (purple), coconut plantations (light grey), bush and scattered shrubs (light green), dry fields (brown), rice fields irrigated the whole year (dark blue), water (light blue) and unclassified (black). A supervised classification of selected scenes was then done on an image classifier by Dipix Systems Ltd. and this produced a 3-colour vegetation map. A study of the two areas, rice irrigated only in the rainy season and rice irrigated all the year, showed that there was quite a large difference in the two dates. It would appear from looking at the June map that most of the rice is rainfed rice, but this was because both classes were ripening and close to harvest and they both had similar spectral signatures. In October, on the other hand, rainfed rice fields were dry and left fallow, while the permanently irrigated rice fields were growing a second crop. A knowledge of harvesting practices therefore allowed the two classes to be differentiated. The rainfed areas were calculated to be about 55,607 hectares. This figure combined with climatic data and yield statistics from previous years will enable agricultural managers to forecast future total yields and so to estimate to what extent the harvest must be supplemented from other sources.

Apart from the scientific achievement of this project, it was interesting as an example of international cooperation. The study was conducted within the framework of the National Resource Survey and Mapping Project of Indonesia and was assisted by the International Development Research Centre of Canada. Professional assistance was given by a member of the Forest Management Institute of the Department of Fisheries and the Environment of Canada, who spent 2 years in Indonesia. Since in Indonesia there were no facilities for processing Landsat computer tapes

and since Canada was a long way away, help was forth-
coming in the preliminary stage of the programme from
Japan, who produced the maps giving an unsupervised
classification. The satellite data came from the U.S.A.,
who launched the satellite in the first place. This
information was only one part of the picture; allied with
further data from aerial photography using panchromatic
and colour-infrared film, the resultant imagery should be of
great assistance to Indonesia in the planning of her future
prosperity.

Experiments carried out in northern Manitoba and the
Mackenzie Valley (N.W.T.) show the value of remote sensing
for the mapping of permafrost areas. In the arctic and sub-
arctic environments, satellite imagery is indirectly able to
detect such areas quite successfully by reflection of light
from the associated vegetation; further south where the
relationship between permafrost, vegetation, drainage and
soil patterns is more complex, Landsat pictures have proved
useful in pointing out areas that may later be looked at by
other methods. The best information for permafrost regions
seems to be given by airborne colour-infrared in conjunction
with standard black and white photography, and in some
cases with thermal infrared scanning.

The study of permafrost and other ground features has a
very practical value in construction projects - in choosing
suitable routes for roads and pipelines, for example. A
pipeline costs a considerable amount of money per mile to
build. If it is located on bad terrain, swamp or muskeg,
costs may increase by some hundreds of thousands of dollars
per mile. Care should be taken to avoid locating it in areas
of hard bedrock where expensive blasting may be necessary.
Landsat data was used recently by engineers studying
possible routes for the proposed natural gas pipeline from
the Queen Elizabeth Archipelago. The photographs clearly
outlined unusual features in the relief and the effects of
snow formation and ice movement on the terrain. The
choice of a suitable route for a highway may also be helped
by satellite imagery, particularly in the North, where routes
are long and several alternative possibilities exist. A study
of drainage patterns can reduce the number of bridges, or
the number of culverts, which are both costly.

Remote sensing methods can be used to advantage in the

planning of transmission line routes. For example, B.C. Hydro wanted to take a 500 kV line from Liard to Prince George by going westwards across the Rockies and down the Rocky Mountain Trench. They were concerned that they should create as little disturbance as possible to the existing environment. Several factors are involved here. There are sociological considerations, such as the traditional rights of the Indian population to fishing and hunting grounds, the possible damage to recreation areas, to forestry and agriculture, and the disturbance of wild life habitats. You may say "How can a cable slung up on pylons way above people's heads disturb anything?" But, the very fact that roads would have to be made to allow workers to instal the lines in the first place and maintain them afterwards means that an access would be given for the general public to get into the heart of the wilderness; something would inevitably be destroyed for ever. It was considered important that the impact of the human element should be minimized and that the feeding habits of goats, sheep and caribou should not be disturbed.

Since so little was known about some of these remote and inaccessible regions, the first thing to do was to gather information from all possible sources to find out more about them. The most economical way of getting a quick over-view seemed to be to take a look at Landsat imagery. A geologist and a biologist experienced in interpretation were asked to look at and classify wild life habitats. Although a fair amount of data gathered by conventional methods was already available for the southern part of B.C., very little was known of northern regions. It was considered that the correlation of known land capability areas in the south with the unknown areas in the north would be practical on a cost-benefit basis only if satellite imagery could be digitally processed and interpreted accurately.

Since the areas were mountainous, there was a problem with long shadows obscuring some of the land detail, and so the scientists had to select Landsat imagery for a time of the year when the sun was high in the sky. By computer image techniques they were able to divide areas of terrain and vegetation into categories needed for wildlife habitat classification. Alpine grassland is particularly desirable for goats and sheep, and it was found possible to map these areas with an accuracy of about 60% to 75%. For about 25% of the area it was not possible to get a high accuracy because the vegetation patterns were complex, containing several different types of plants. This study proved the value of satellite imagery for such purposes; thousands of dollars were saved since the computer tapes were already available at low cost, and the preliminary stages of the study could be completed quickly without the need for extensive field work. It is now possible to accumulate and maintain data banks which in turn can be used for future investigations, as well as for the monitoring of environmental changes during and after the construction phases of any building project.

In installing power lines the engineers also want to know as much as possible about the nature of the terrain -whether it is hard rock or muskeg, whether there are any existing logging roads which could be used for transportation of materials or, indeed, whether there are any nearby sources of supplies and adequate amounts of fresh water. All of these factors can be detected using Landsat imagery.

The location of paper mills is another case in point. They should be built as close to a wood supply as possible, consistent with the ability to ship the finished product out to world markets expeditiously. Remote sensing will allow management to assess the quantity and type of wood, to see how much has been burned over or is in poor health, to see the extent of areas that have already been logged, and to see how many logging roads are already available to them. Again, satellite images are able to make a first selection, which can later be followed up by airborne sensors.

Landsat with its periodic repetitive imagery has provided us with an unexcelled opportunity of watching dynamic processes, such as the effect of construction schemes on the environment. Before being able to assess the damage to surrounding areas, we must know what they were like before any activity took place; in other words, we need to establish a baseline as a reference point. Satellite imagery is now bringing in data that will allow us to construct such baselines. We were fortunate in being able to collect imagery on the James Bay hydroelectric project from the beginning, and imagery obtained on a continuous basis throughout the work have provided us with an interesting pictorial history. Landsat - 2 and - 3 images were used to monitor and study the LG2 dam during the filling period, which began on November 27, 1979. They illustrated the main stages of the dam filling. Two of the images were analyzed in some detail. One, of February 15, 1980, was analyzed with respect to the mapping of the vegetation uplifted by the ice. Another, of July 26, was analyzed in order to evaluate turbidity conditions and the location of partially flooded vegetation.

We are now collecting data on the Beaufort Sea area and other parts of the Arctic where we may expect to see more activity in the near future. As well as being able to monitor any environmental changes, either natural or manmade, the satellite will provide data which will comprise an invaluable fund of knowledge for companies wishing to establish themselves in the area. Little is known at present. Engineers will be bringing in expensive mining equipment and will want to know the best place for installing it, the best time of the year for bringing it in and the best route for getting it there. The vast amount of data being gathered by Landsat will allow us to answer many questions of this nature which until now we have been unable to do.

The limitations of the present sensors mounted on the satellite platform for gathering information in the far North during the long, dark days of winter and under adverse cloud conditions have already been mentioned, so that in the study of dynamic processes here radar again has much to offer. It is ideal for reconnaissance work and for routine surveillance. The environmental protection agencies are interested in it for regular observation, because it is very difficult to keep track of who is up in the Arctic or sub-Arctic digging a hole or putting in an oil well. Apart from being efficacious, radar is also economical for such purposes. With its wide sweep it can cover large areas of ground very quickly. To take an example, at a height of 2,000 metres, normal vertical photography would give a coverage of about 3,000 metres, wide-angle photography about 4,000 metres, superwide-angle about 6,000 metres, and reconnaissance SLAR systems with a 40° coverage about 20,000 metres. For the same flying time and same expense, the coverage would thus be much greater. Of course, the resolution would be correspondingly less, but this is the price we have to pay. With the development of synthetic aperture systems with greater resolution the coverage/resolution relationship could be considerably improved.

It is also possible to study a number of other dynamic processes in this way. We have already seen that by means of thermal infrared scanners mounted in aircraft we can forecast volcanic activity and we can gain information on a regular basis from the Data Collection System in Landsat. Instruments may be mounted on a platform on or in a volcano and data may be transmitted to the satellite to be in turn transmitted to earth. In this way scientists were able to predict the eruption of Fuego, a volcano in Guatemala, in February, 1973. Unfortunately no such information was available before the Iceland eruption; we have been able to survey the damage wrought only after the event.

Other catastrophic events about which we may be able to get some forewarning are landslides. Although it is difficult to get positive indications that a landslide is about to take place, we can establish certain criteria for assessing the susceptibility of terrain to this sort of behaviour and so be on the look-out for it. First of all, steep slopes, particularly in a clay soil, are susceptible to slide movements. These slopes may be man-made or they may have evolved naturally. Examples of man-made conditions are the disastrous slide at Asbestos in 1974, and the big slide about 5 miles east of Hawkesbury, which took place when Highway 17 was being built in the early 1950's. Natural slopes may be created by the erosion of tributaries running into river channels. The study of drainage patterns and water flow that give rise to landslides may be helped by airborne sensors, colour-infrared photography, thermal infrared scanning and radar, and also by Landsat imagery; changes in land conditions may be monitored to some extent by the repetitive coverage provided by satellites.

Since the various remote-sensing devices are able to provide so much information on the nature of the earth's surface, the question comes to mind "Can they help a geologist in the location of new sources of minerals, such as nickel, iron, oil and gas?"

The answer may at first sight seem a little disappointing.

In the early days of exploration by satellite, many geologists felt that these methods had little future. However a few optimists persisted in their efforts to get as much information out of a Landsat image as possible, until to-day remote sensing by satellite is a recognized aid in locating valuable minerals. This has been achieved by new techniques of image analysis and increased experience in interpretation. Seldom is it possible to look at a Landsat image and say "Eureka ! There is a gold mine.", but, taken in conjunction with other information, observations from space represent another tool - an important tool - to unlock the secrets of the earth below. Most mineral deposits are below the surface and so can seldom be detected directly. However, a geologist is trained in the ability to deduce what is below from what he sees on top, and many of the surface details are able to tell him a great deal about the physical and chemical properties of the underlying rocks and soils. Shapes, textures, colours and patterns are all related to the geological processes that produced them. It is therefore all-important that a geologist should make use of any form of remote sensing that will give him any relevant data. No one method will tell him everything, but almost every method will tell him something. He is familiar with aerial photography, both from planes and, in special cases, from helicopters. Conventional photography has been used for over half a century and is now being supplemented with new types of film, multispectral scanners, infrared scanners, and so on. When weather conditions for photography are unfavorable, he can go over to radar, though this is more expensive; microwaves have an added advantage in being able to detect differences in rock texture which may be a clue to structure. Different minerals have different emissivities and heat capacities, so that thermal infrared scanning can contribute some meaningful data on chemical constituents, physical features, geothermal activity, soil moisture, water drainage systems, etc. In the past, special airborne instruments have been carried; magnetometers were used for locating iron deposits and some ores commonly associated with iron; gamma-ray spectrometers were used in estimating the abundance of potassium, uranium, and thorium in the surface crust; electromagnetic instruments showed the presence of highly conductive materials. Now to this impressive array of equipment we can add satellite imagery.

Landsat imagery is still relatively new, and getting the most out of every picture requires experience. The terrain is frequently covered by plant growth, and it has been argued that this fact is detrimental to the recognition of rocks beneath. However, geologists are learning that vegetative covering can be used to their advantage. The soil on which it grows will affect its colour, shape and general health and so provide one more clue to what lies underneath. Some metals are toxic to plants, while others encourage growth. There are some plants, called indicator plants, which grow preferentially over a particular metal, such as copper, for instance. The spectral signature of a plant with a high content of one mineral may be very different from that of the same plant grown in another area. Therefore vegetation anomalies on a Landsat image should always be studied with care. Measurement of the diameter of crowns of trees may indicate a certain type of mineralization. Certainly the appearance of trees in otherwise barren land would suggest the presence of underground streams. During a search for underground water around the Dead Sea area, the presence of 7 fig trees was detected on a Landsat picture and led to the discovery of such water. You may say "Surely you cannot see a fig tree on a Landsat image; the scale is too small." That is true, but the appearance of a group of trees against an otherwise barren background will alter the particular pixel slightly and alert the scientists to a different condition that should be examined more closely.

Although vegetative covering sometimes makes terrain features a little more difficult to recognize, individual geologists all have their own tricks for tackling the problem. It may be possible to use stereo imagery. Adjacent images would have to have the requisite amount of overlap for stereo viewing. This would generally only be obtainable for scenes north of the 60° parallel, or in particularly favorable cases the 55° parallel, where adjacent images overlap sufficiently. Alternatively it is sometimes possible to create an artificial stereoscopic effect. This can be done by going back to the original computer tapes and offsetting the scene pixel by pixel and then viewing it alongside the

PLATE I. Effluent from Pickering Power Plant. Density Sliced
Thermal Infrared Image.

Colour Code:

☐ above 17°C   ■ 12.10°C — 13.32°C

■ 15.77°C — 17°C   ■ 10.88°C — 12.10°C

■ 14.55°C — 15.77°C   ▨ 9.66°C — 10.88°C

■ 13.32°C — 14.55°C   ☐ below 9.66°C

(see page 63)

168

PLATE II. Microwave Map of the North Pole taken from Nimbus-5
Satellite.

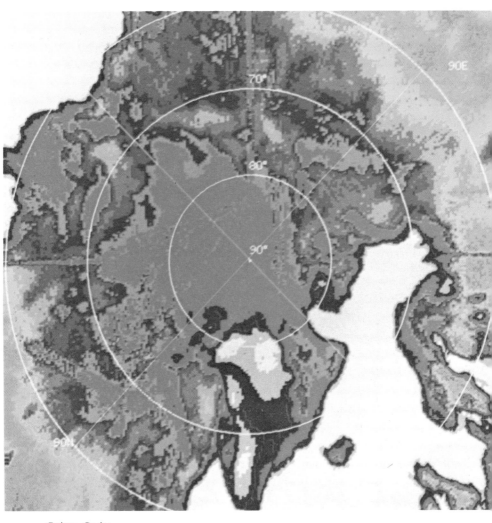

Colour Code:

■ 310K	■ 253K	■ 248K	■ 243K	■ 236K	■ 229K	■ 209K	178K
■ 309K	■ 252K	■ 247K	■ 242K	■ 235K	■ 227K	■ 208K	164K
■ 256K	■ 251K	■ 246K	■ 241K	■ 233K	■ 226K	■ 194K	□ 163K
■ 255K	■ 250K	■ 245K	■ 239K	■ 232K	■ 224K	■ 193K	□ 0K
■ 254K	■ 249K	■ 244K	■ 238K	■ 230K	■ 223K	■ 179K	

          (see page 67)

Polar Map of North Pole. Key to PLATE II.

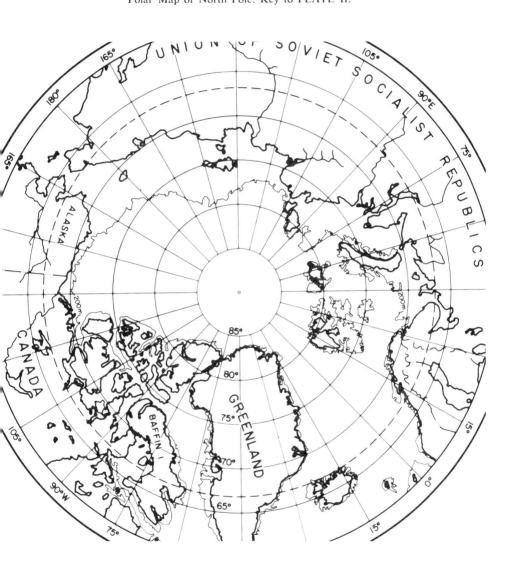

Note: An overlay can be made of this map by tracing the outline on a clear piece of plastic or thin tracing paper. If it is then placed over the coloured image of PLATE II, the location of ice masses may be seen.

170

PLATE III. Landsat-I Image of Montreal Area.

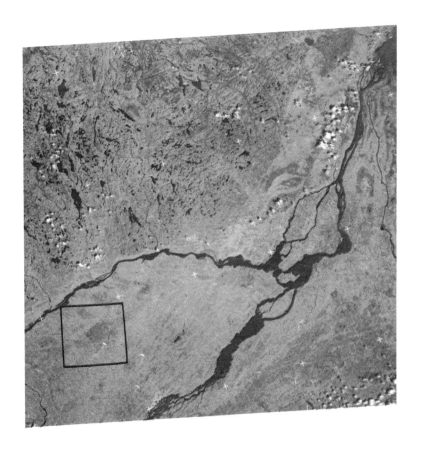

  (see page 150)

Key to Interpretation of PLATE III.

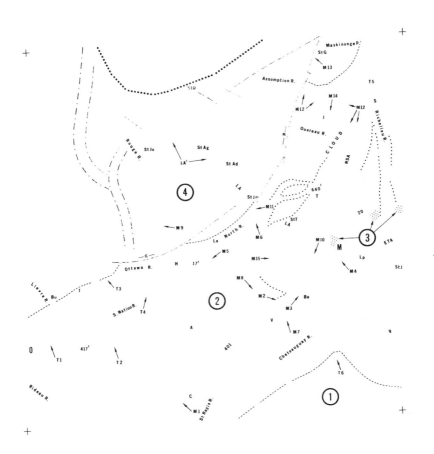

Note: If making an overlay of this key note that the four +'s at the corners correspond to the four corners of the photograph. Key to the above letters and numbers is given on the next page.

Interpretation of key points of Plate III.

Landsat A 3rd September 1972   MSS bands 456 (Color Infrared)

Physiographic units and boundaries

① Adirondacks
② St. Lawrence Lowlands
③ Monteregian Hills
④ Canadian Shield

.... Boundary between Forest Regions B7 (Boreal forest — Missinaibi Cabonga section) and L4 (Great Lakes — St. Lawrence mixed forest-Laurentian section).
.... Edge of the St. Lawrence Lowland
— — — Major faults
— G — Grenville
— R — Rawdon
= = = = Fold structures in the Grenville series
.... Distributary channels and shorelines of the post-glacial marine transgression (Champlain Sea)

Settlements and Urban areas

A	—	Alexandria	S	—	Sorel
Be	—	Beauharnois	StAd	—	Ste Adèle
Bu	—	Buckingham	StAg	—	Ste. Agathe
C	—	Cornwall	StD	—	St.Donat
H	—	Hawkesbury	StG	—	St. Gabriel
J	—	Joliette	StJ	—	St. Jean
La	—	Lachute	StJm	—	St. Jérôme
Lp	—	Laprairie	StJo	—	St. Jovite
M	—	Montréal	StT	—	Ste. Thérèse
O	—	Ottawa	T	—	Terrebonne

Highways

9	
17'	(under construction)
20	
401	
417'	(under construction)
640'	(under construction)
LA	Laurentian Autoroute
LA'	" "
	(under construction)
ETA	Eastern Townships Autoroute
NSA	North Shore Autoroute

Manmade features

M1   Barnhart Island power dam
M2   Soulanges Canal
M3   Beauharnois power dam
M4   St. Lawrence Seaway
M5   Carillon power dam
M6   Montréal II International Airport (under construction)
M7   Beauharnois Ship Canal
M8   Sand and gravel pit
M9   Canadian Refractories — Kilmar mine
M10 Montréal International Airport — Dorval
M11 Canadian Carborundum — St. Canut open pit
M12 Joliette tobacco farming area — open field landscape
M13 Mount Royal Paving Co. — open pit
M14 Beaudry Limestone quarry
M15 St. Lawrence Columbian and Metals Co. open pit

Terrain features

T1   Mer Bleue peat bog
T2   Casselman earth flow
T3   Baie de la Pentecôte (blue green coloration from concentration of sediment in suspension and low dissolved oxygen content)
T4   Alfred peat bog
T5   Estuarine delta of St. Lawrence
T6   Covey Hill glacial drainage channel

PLATE IV. Landsat-I Image of the Mackenzie Delta.

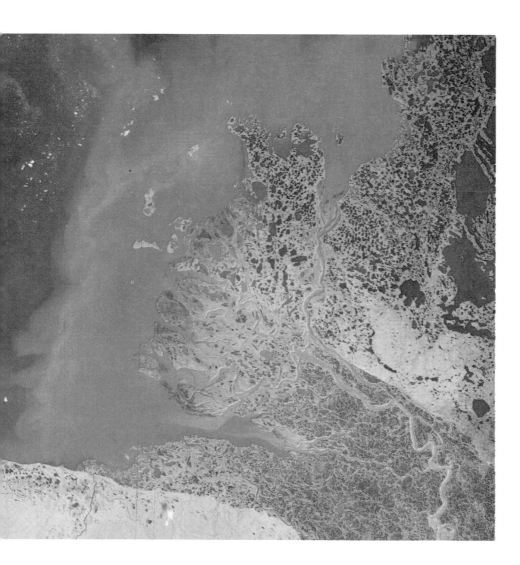

Courtesy of Canada Centre for Remote Sensing

(see page 204)

174

PLATE V. Automated Map of the Nova Scotia Coastline.

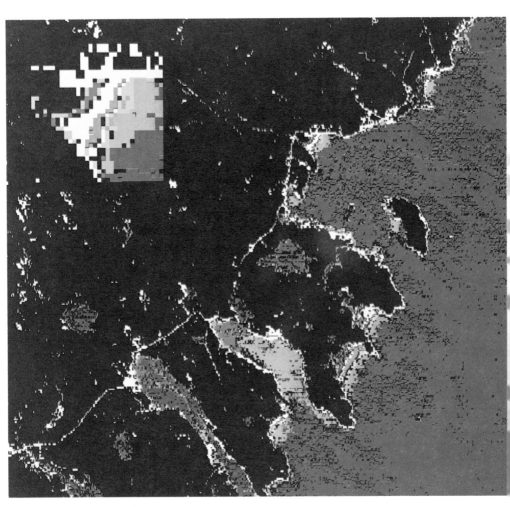

Colour Code:

■ Clear Water

▨ Dry Sand (Highly Reflective)

■ Mud Flats

▨ Shallow Water with a Sand Bottom

▨ Organic Material in Water

▨ Very Shallow Water (Adjacent to Beaches)

☐ Low Order Vegetation Sparse to Bare Earth

■ An Atmospheric Phenomenon — Probably Fog

■ Overlap of Themes

■ Unmapped

Courtesy of Canada Centre for Remote Sensing

(see page 139)

PLATE VI. Automated Map of the Larose Forest Area.

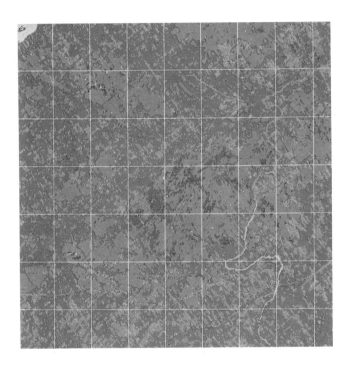

Colour Code:

■ Deciduous Forest ■ Other Agricultural Land

■ Coniferous Forest ▢ Water

■ Ploughed Land and Roads ■ Unclassified

Courtesy of Forest Management Institute, Canada Forestry Service (see page 231)

176

PLATE VII. Automated Map of the Larose Forest Area.
(Hand Coloured)

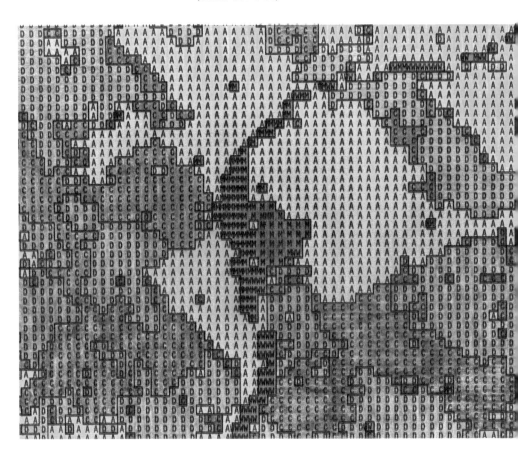

A   Agricultural Land   W   Water

C   Coniferous Forest   M   Bare Soil & Muddy Water

D   Deciduous Forest   U   Unknown

Courtesy of Forest Management Institute, Canada Forestry Service   (see page 231)

PLATE VIII. Aerial photograph of Experimental Potato Plots infected with Late Blight.

Courtesy of Research Branch, Agriculture Canada

(see page 221)

178

PLATE IX. a) Landsat Image   b) Seasat Image

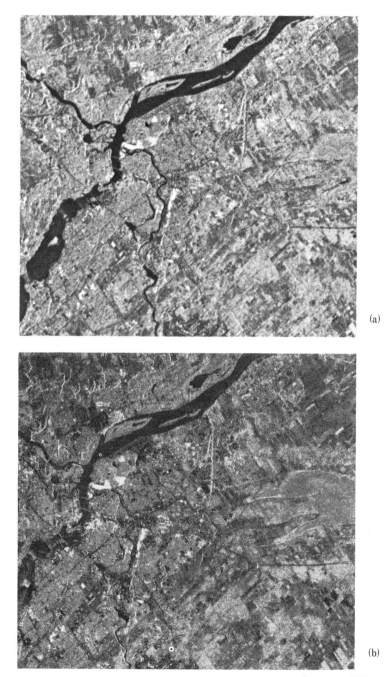

(a)

(b)

(see page 135)

PLATE X. Composite of Landsat and Seasat Imagery.

Courtesy of MacDonald Dettwiler and Associates, Ltd.

(see page 135)

180

PLATE XI. Gypsum Deposits.

cover Photo

Courtesy of Reimchen Sursicial Geology, Ltd.
(now Pegasus Earth Sensing Corp.)

(see page 186)

PLATE XII. Wallops Oil Spill.

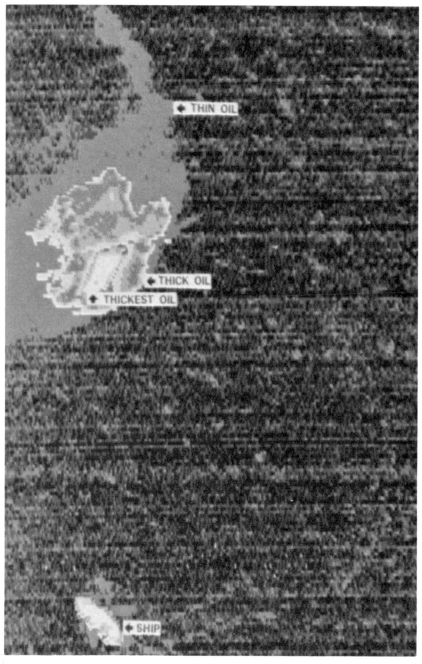

Courtesy of Canada Center for Remote Sensing

(see page 214)'

182

PLATE XIII. A Soil Study in Alberta.

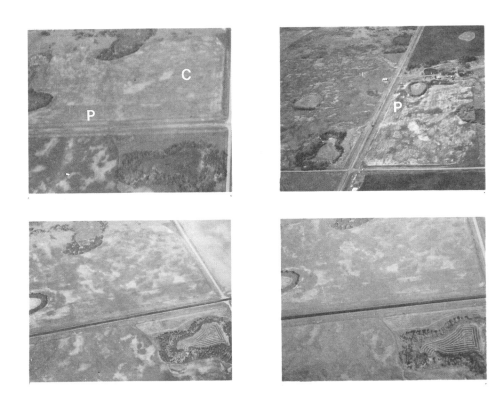

Color and color infrared photographs of Site 6 taken July 18 (top) and August 17 (bottom) 1977.

Courtesy of the Alberta Remote Sensing Center and the
Department of Soil Science, University of Alberta

(see page 225)

PLATE XIV. Grazing Lands in Alberta.

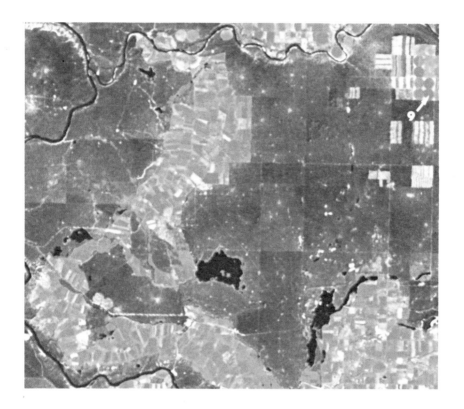

ırtesy of Canada Centre for Remote Sensing and the Alberta Remote Sensing Center (see page 227)

184

PLATE XV. Forest Fire Fuel Map.

W — Black   — Water   S — Blue Grey — Mixed softwood
R — Red   — Recent clearcut   with darker areas
O — Yellow   — Older clearcut   indicating pure
H — Light Green — Mixed hardwood   stands.
                 with lighter yellow-
                 green tones indi-
                 cating pure stands

Note the transition zones that are evident between major classes of forest cover and the
similarity in appearance to standard colour aerial photography.

Courtesy of Canada Center for Remote Sensing
and The Forest Fire Research Institute of Canada   (see page 235)

original through a stereoscope. Sometimes it may help to turn the Landsat image around and look at it in the direction of the sun so that the shadows always fall on the valleys on the far side of the ridges. If there is little relief and the shadows are weak, it would probably be helpful to obtain an image with a light dusting of snow. In this way the north side of the ridges and mountain crests and slopes will be readily visible. Obtaining Landsat images at different times of the year is also useful because of the vegetation changes that occur throughout the changing seasons. The changes can be monitored by repetitive viewing of images obtained on different dates. The use of change detection techniques referred to in Chapter VI would enable these changes only to be imaged and nothing else.

Methods are being developed which allow the thickness of muskeg or the amount of regrowth (i.e. the total biomass) to be calculated. Since the removal of the overburden is a very expensive part of a mining operation, this would mean a considerable reduction in the ultimate costs. An example is in the Tar Sands where millions of dollars have been spent in muskeg removal. It would be a great help to know before starting an operation how much is there. At present the only way of finding out is to drill - and that is expensive.

If follows that valid interpretations, being largely arrived at by inference, require a geologist with very special qualifications. He must have both a good imagination and a good memory. He must remember all the scenes he has viewed before; he can then spot situations in one case that he has seen elsewhere - sometimes years before. He can study a scene which has a particular combination of features of terrain or plant growth and be able to say "Ah! I remember seeing a similar condition in a picture I saw last year, and that suggested the presence of copper, perhaps, or uranium". This needs a good memory. Or on looking at a structure of mountain ridges that were formed when the earth solidified and shrank he may ask himself "Now, how was that landscape formed?" and "If I were a mineral in solution, where would I go?" This needs a good imagination.

It is appropriate at this stage to look at the way a geological exploration is carried out and to consider a few actual examples. Examples are sometimes difficult to find in this area because, for obvious reasons, the results are often confidential; mining companies do not want everyone else knowing what they are up to.

A mineral exploration project is an extremely costly process. For example, it took one company 9 or 10 million dollars to discover one uranium ore body, and, if the search had not been successful 9 or 10 million dollars would have been wasted. Oil exploration is similarly expensive. A search for minerals takes place in several stages. First of all there is a regional geological reconnaissance stage, which is followed by geophysical and geochemical surveys. This in turn will be followed by detailed site field mapping and drilling operations. Since each succeeding phase of this programme is more expensive than the preceding one, it is important that each should limit the area to be covered in the next. This is where a judicious choice of remote sensing methods comes in. The first stage can most economically be carried out by satellite with its small-scale synoptic view of large areas. The correct interpretation at this stage of ridges, folds, faults, intersecting linears, etc., can result in considerable savings in the next stage. The second stage in turn can best be accomplished by aerial photography, either black and white or colour, infrared scanning or radar in aircraft flying at different altitudes. In the third stage all known information is gathered from all sources and fitted together by overlay maps. This will probably start off with a thorough search of the literature, a study of existing geological maps and the acquisition of aeromagnetic and gravimetric data. All can be registered on appropriate overlays or fed into a computer programme. Anomalous areas defined by intersection of geophysical, geochemical and/or computer assisted spectral values are plotted. The final stage of drilling will test the validity of the conclusions reached.

As an example, a company was looking for a source of gypsum in the southern Canadian Rockies. The manager wanted this to be close to his manufacturing operation, easy of access and close to transportation routes. Since gypsum is a relatively soft material, it seemed reasonable to suppose that the landforms would be different from those of the harder limestone around it. Since gypsum is more soluble in water than the surrounding limestone, it seemed reasonable to suppose that the slopes of the hills would be different. Also vegetation over areas rich in gypsum might appear to be different from that over limestone areas. With these ideas in mind a geologist generated a digital computer Landsat image (Plate XI). The image covers an area 185 km square, situated in the Lussier valley, northeast of Cranbrook, B.C. It shows snow-crested mountains and a valley towards the west of the picture, through which flows a river; we can see a beige-coloured area here and a sprinkling of yellow dots. The yellow dots, which were selected by an image analyzer as described in Chapter VI, represent areas underlain by gypsoferous soils or gypsum-bearing rock formations. Initially the computer training of known gypsum areas had produced a number of anomalous regions and it was suspected that the gypsum was stratiform (i.e. contained between and within certain rock types). A computer programme was written whereby after filtering out extraneous noise and vegetation spectra, a ratio of the composite bands was obtained. Anomalous points were thus produced and overlaid on to the appropriate pixels of the image. Subsequent geological mapping, including geo-chemistry, geophysics and drilling showed that these large clusters of yellow were areas rich in gypsum. The beige background in the valley showed clear-cut forest areas.

As a result of this study more than 56 prime exploration targets were delineated. Subsequent field operations proved that 3 of these had marketable amounts of gypsum. Two of the deposits appeared to be close together and later drilling showed that they were, in fact, joined below ground. The whole deposit turned out to contain over 100 million tons.

So we can see that although satellite imagery seldom permits a deposit to be discovered directly, it does play an important role in the initial stage; it represents an economical way of getting a quick overview for planning further investigations. Also the fact that all the data is recorded on computer tapes makes it convenient for combining satellite data in a computer programme with data obtained from other sources.

CHAPTER VIII

RIVERS, LAKES AND SEAS

Water is one of the world's most valuable but probably most ill-used resources. It is so readily available and so cheap that, except under occasional conditions of low rainfall, we in Canada take it for granted. We waste it and pollute it. In some parts of the world it is less plentiful and thus more highly valued and better looked after; with the increase in the world population and improvements in our standard of living, we are going to need more and more water for drinking, for carrying away wastes, for agriculture and for industry. Water is needed for transporting ships, and as a habitat for fish, water fowl and other forms of aquatic life. It acts as a heat reservoir in cold weather and as a cooling medium in the summer. In the future we are going to need more water of high quality at a time when our increased activity seems to be conspiring to lower this quality. Water running off from agricultural lands into the streams and rivers contains fertilizers, pesticides and animal wastes; many industries are located on rivers for the very reason that they wish to take in large quantities of water for their process operations and to use large volumes of water to carry away their industrial wastes. Most of our large cities are located on rivers, and much of the sewage from urban communities ends up there.

We will first consider our inland lakes and rivers containing fresh water. It is obvious that we must set about managing this important commodity a great deal better than we have been doing. First of all we want to be able to assess the extent of our resources and to seek new sources of water, and secondly we need to be able to monitor its quality. Remote sensing methods are able to help our water management engineers in both of these areas.

The amount of water available varies with the time of year, and so a remote-sensing method which would enable us to map these changes on a repetitive basis throughout the year over the whole of the country is badly needed. Landsat seems like the answer to a prayer. We have seen that as we go from band 4 through to band 7 of the multispectral scanner on the satellite, the penetrating power of light rays into water decreases. With the shorter wavelengths of band 4 (500–600 nanometres) we are able to see things below the water level and in the case of shallow waters we are actually able to see the bottom. Because water has a very low reflectivity for light of long wavelength, band 7 is particularly good at giving us images which show a strong contrast between water and the surrounding land masses. A suitable combination of several images at different wavelengths gives us a great deal of data. The scale of 1:250,000 which can be obtained from satellite imagery is quite adequate for mapping large areas of water, but for smaller streams we would have to supplement the data with that from airborne sensors.

In Canada we have a large number of lakes covering hundreds of thousands of square miles, but since many of these are inaccessible they are not all useful. Images from Landsat have shown us new water bodies and promising areas which could be investigated more closely with aircraft, using infrared photography, infrared scanners and radar. By giving us a bird's eye view of the whole country Landsat is able to show quickly the position of these lakes and their geographical relationship to the urban and agricultural areas which require fresh water supplies. Since it is the volume of water in which we are interested rather than the area, work is proceeding on ways in which this can be worked out, at least approximately. It can already be done for shallow waters by measuring water depth with a laser bathymeter, or by combining the data from bands 4 and 7 of satellite imagery. The volume of water in a lake will also be a factor in determining the rate at which it cools, so that thermal infrared measurements can contribute to our information, as may also radar measurements on ice thickness in the winter time. Data from the ground-based data collection stations, relayed through the satellite play an important role. Streamflow data, water level and rainfall figures may be transmitted to the satellite, which then telemeters this to the ground receiving stations where it is combined with other data for distribution to those interested. All of this information will be invaluable to water resource management.

The location not only of surface waters but also indirectly of underground streams can be indicated by satellite. Knowing something of the terrain structure -types of rock and fracture zones - geologists can make an educated guess as to the whereabouts of underground water; there are many instances where successful drillings have followed identification of rock types from Landsat imagery. Some hitherto unsuspected sources are now providing ground water for agricultural purposes - an immediately practical result of untold value to a rancher whose production capabilities may be limited by lack of adequate water supplies.

Infrared photography, or **thermography,** as it is more properly called has proved an excellent method of mapping fresh water springs. As we saw in the infrared photograph in Figure 16, when water is warmer than the surrounding land it stands out as light against a dark background. In winter the water seeping up from within the ground, or bubbling up as in a spring will again be warmer and show up as light against a dark background. Making use of this principle, the Ontario Centre for Remote Sensing successfully gathered information and mapped discharge areas over the Nine Mile River (formerly Lucknow River) watershed in Southwestern Ontario. There had been some concern that trout streams in that area were reduced in flow, and that, as a result of an increase in the number of ponds in the area, the water was becoming too warm for trout. The question became why. Was it because the farmer in his desire to drain his land properly was leading the water away elsewhere? Was it because forests and wetlands were being cleared? Had in fact the streams really been diminishing at all, or was it just that things in the past so often look better in retrospect? The whole problem needed close examination. To obtain the information on the ground for even one modest trout stream would be time-consuming and expensive. Remote sensing of some form or another seemed to offer the prospect of a quicker and cheaper alternative. In 1977 the Maitland Valley Conservation Authority asked the Ontario Centre for Remote Sensing to cooperate in the project to get as much information as cheaply as possible to help in the management of their water resources.

Thermography obtained by a scanner operated from a low flying aircraft was the means chosen. The best time of the year for carrying out such an operation is after freeze-up when all bodies of water not near a warm spring are frozen. A mantle of snow on the ground presents a more or less uniform temperature and therefore a uniform dark background, against which the warmer water can easily be recognized as a white feature on the image. Trees and other objects above ground level can be located quite well above the snow; they will show as lighter shades of grey against the darker grey of the cold snow. Figure 53 represents a thermograph of an area with several hot spots as marked by arrows. It may be seen that the springs are discharging enough water to form small streams. This image was obtained at night between 10.15 p.m. and 12.45 a.m.. The best time for taking thermographs is about 3 or 4 hours after sunset, because by then any heat gathered throughout the day has been lost and the background is as uniform as possible. Thermography was obtained over the whole area and was examined in conjunction with standard black and white aerial photographs of a scale 1:15,840 and topographic maps of 1:50,000. The sites of discharge of underground waters were then located on a 1:5,000 scale Rural Fill Line map provided by the Maitland Conservation Authority.

The results showed that aerial thermography is an excellent method for the mapping of ground water discharges of all kinds.

In Canada a great deal of our fresh water comes from melting ice and snow in the springtime, sometimes producing flooding of disastrous proportions. While it may not be possible to prevent the snow from melting (and indeed we would not wish to do so!), observations of the build-up of snow in the winter and the rate of melting in the spring would provide a warning to those likely to be affected by flooding. Landsat is able to provide us with such information. Snowline altitudes may be determined within about 200 ft., and the area covered by snow within a few per cent. Even better assessments of depth can be made in places where there are landmarks of a known height; we can watch the disappearance of these landmarks on successive passes of the satellite. In the first stage of melting the

Courtesy of Ontario Centre for Remote Sensing.

Figure 53. Thermogram showing Discharges of Underground Waters.

surface of snow or ice becomes covered with a thin film of water. This lowers the reflectance considerably and can be detected from satellite images. From all this data, much of it gathered from inaccessible areas of such enormous extent that continuous vigilance by aircraft would be impractical, engineers can calculate approximately the total amount and rate of run-off. The likelihood of flooding is sometimes indicated by the degree to which the soil is saturated with moisture. The run-off will be much faster if the top few inches of soil are already wet. Radar is an excellent way of indicating soil moisture conditions and useful information is also given by photographs in the near infrared bands from either aircraft or satellite sensors. The rapidity with which Landsat images can be analyzed is a great asset. In emergency situations these photographs can be interpreted within a few hours, and the data from ground-based data collection stations within about half-an-hour of receipt. This gives time for engineers to control the water release from reservoirs and to take other measures to avert some of the worst effects of flooding.

All of this information would be valuable not only for flood victims but for hydro-electric engineers for both existing and proposed power schemes. It would permit more effective management of reservoir storage and river flow for irrigation, human and industrial uses. By means of satellites water resource measurements can now be made on a global scale and should be of great help to hydrologists, enabling them to acquire a new understanding of the world's fresh water supply.

Ice thickness measurements can now be made to a fair degree of accuracy. Landsat will give us a small scale overall view of ice disposition, but to gauge its thickness we have to use airborne sensors such as infrared scanners, or better still microwave radiometers, or radar. Measurements of ice thickness would not only offer another means of estimating the availability of fresh water in the spring, but would be a great help in connection with our waterways. Anything which would contribute to our knowledge and thus aid the realization of the dream of year-round navigation in the St. Lawrence Seaway, for example, would enable us to take a big step forward. Radar would tell us also where the ice was thick enough to support heavy vehicles or structures, where the thin spots were for the ice-breakers to push their way through; it could guide shipping through channels in the ice.

Glaciers are an important source of water in many parts of the world. It is estimated that in Canada we have between 70,000 and 100,000 individual glaciers ranging in size from 83 square metres to 3,900 square kilometres. These are mostly located in the Rockies and Arctic regions, and contain as much water as all the Great Lakes combined. The mapping of these glaciers was originally done over a long period of time by aircraft, but it would be impossible to carry out the regular monitoring of such a large number in this way. Once again satellite imagery with its regular, repetitive overview is an invaluable tool for the glaciologist. Satellite photographs gave the first indications of fracturing in the surface of the Tweedsmuir glacier in February, 1973. This is a medium sized glacier about 3 km long and 71 km wide, sitting astride the British Columbia, Yukon and Alaska boundaries. Since that time the glacier was seen to accelerate its pace of advance. Fears were expressed that it might block the Alzek River and cause extensive flooding. Fortunately that did not happen. The motion of the glacier was closely and anxiously watched by both aircraft and satellite. While it did in fact cut off the old river, as had been expected, the water was diverted into another channel.

Remote sensing is thus able to tell us a great deal about the quantity of water available to us. What is equally important is that it is also able to give us information on its quality.

The assessment of quality is a rather complicated problem because there are so many forms of pollution. Among the chemical pollutants we have effluents from factories which lower the quality of water for drinking and may be toxic to fish and other forms of aquatic life. They are often unsightly and damaging to recreational areas. Phosphates and fertilizers have the effect of increasing aquatic growth, thus impeding the flow of rivers; we have bacterial contaminants, such as human and animal wastes and other organic materials which in decomposing use up the oxygen in the water; we have oil slicks from accidental spills, and sediment from dredging and other operations. We also have thermal pollution. All of these require a different approach for their detection.

Thermal pollution is probably the simplest to detect. It arises mainly from processing industries and power plants, which by discharging large quantities of warm water cause an increase in the temperature of the lakes and rivers, sometimes beyond what the fish can tolerate. The higher temperature also increases the rate of decomposition of organic materials, thus depleting the oxygen in the water; it also increases the rate of plant and algae growth. As we have seen the best way of detecting small temperature differences is by infrared scanners; the method is very sensitive and can measure changes of a fraction of a degree, as may be seen in Plate I. By means of images obtained from aircraft it is a simple problem to monitor streams of warm effluent from a factory. We can measure the temperature quite accurately and can study the flow patterns in the moving waters. Sometimes a warm stream of water will travel practically unmixed and show a long plume carried many miles into a lake. Sometimes turbulence will cause the cold and warm waters to mix and come to an acceptable temperature very quickly. Knowing what is actually happening is the first step to the correction of the condition.

The detection of unsuspected thermal pollution is perhaps as important as the monitoring of known outfalls from industry. For example, in large stockyards or poultry farms the run-off from the land containing a considerable amount of organic material is generally warmer than the rivers into which it flows. The movement of these waters can be watched with infrared sensors.

As already mentioned industrial effluents are a serious form of water pollution. A great deal of progress has been made in recent years and millions of dollars have been spent by industry in attempting to clean this up, but the problem is far from being completely solved. We have already seen in Chapter II that laser fluorosensors are useful in some cases, notably in paper mills where the discharge contains fluorescent materials. Landsat sensors have also proved useful, and there is at least one case on record where satellite imagery was used as evidence in legal proceedings against a paper mill. Other methods will certainly develop as we learn more about the spectral signatures of various

contaminants. Oil contamination is another hazard which
can be detected by fluorosensors and this will be discussed
further in connection with seawater since most of our oil
spills take place on the oceans.

Chlorophyll and sediment are two common pollutants in
our inland water system. Chlorophyll is an indication of the
biomass in the water. Sediment gives rise to turbidity.
Apart from the fact that we do not like to drink cloudy
water, it is to be deplored because it reduces the amount of
light penetrating to the lower layers. Experiments carried
out at the Canada Centre for Inland Waters using data from
Landsat-I showed that there is a definite correlation
between both turbidity and chlorophyll content, and
reflectance values as obtained by the multispectral scanner.
Band 5 images were found to be the best for studying
turbidity since light of this wavelength penetrates water
better than that of infrared wavelengths. Band 6 and 7
images, on the other hand, were found to be the best for
determining chlorophyll content. Since the infrared rays do
not penetrate water, this must be a surface measurement
only, and is at present restricted to waters where the
chlorophyll content is high. The tests were carried out over
the south-western end of Lake Ontario, at Cootes Paradise,
West Pond and Hamilton Harbour. Computer print-outs
made from Landsat tapes showed clearly patterns of
distribution and mixing; quantitatively the measurements
checked very well with measurements made on actual water
samples. These results showed that satellite imagery has
much to offer in the assessment of water quality. A very
large number of measurements would have been needed to
cover these areas in any other way. Historically the
experiments were of interest because it was the first time
that so much detail was obtained on such a large body of
water at exactly the same moment in time.

While sediment in rivers or lakes may be an undesirable
element when considering water quality, it may serve a
useful purpose when we are studying the dynamic behaviour
of such waters. The silt particles act as tracers for showing
the direction of flow of water currents. A study of
sediment distribution will give information on the way in
which coastlines change, being eroded in one place and built
up in another; they will show the eroding effects of shipping

in narrow passageways such as the St. Lawrence Seaway. This is very important information for land-use planners. It would be disastrous to build a large hotel or condominium on land which would probably not be there in ten years time. Recreational areas and bathing beaches should be built with full knowledge of the changing conditions likely to obtain in the future. Cottagers do not want to invest their money in building on a disappearing land site.

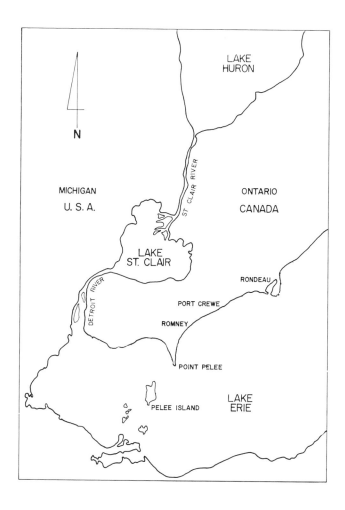

Figure 54. Outline of Lake Erie Area.

It has been possible to use satellite imagery for studying these problems, and again the Great Lakes area was used as our outdoor laboratory. Some quite dramatic results have been obtained by the Canada Centre for Inland Water at Burlington, Ontario. They used digital data recorded on tapes to study the transport of sediment in the Lake Huron-Lake St. Clair-Lake Erie system. Figure 54 shows a sketch of this area. Of particular interest were the conclusions reached regarding the Point Pelee and Rondeau areas.

Figure 55 shows a computer print-out acquired when Landsat passed over it on March 26, 1973. The lighter areas represent the regions containing the highest concentration of sediment, land areas being the lightest of all. Light and turbid areas may be seen along the west shores of Lake Erie,

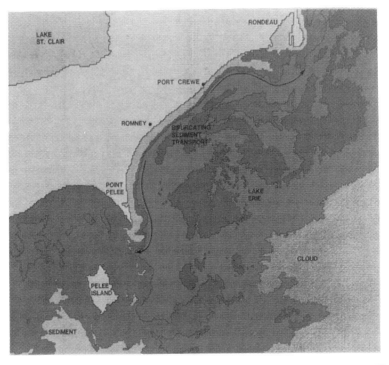

Courtesy of Canada Centre for Inland Waters.

Figure 55. Computer Print-out of Lake Erie Area.

while further out towards the centre the turbidity is diminished. Along a stretch of coast between Romney and Port Crewe the current divides, one part travelling northeast and the other south, both streams carrying sediment with them. The next figure, 56, shows an enlargement of the Point Pelee area: again this is a computer print-out of the data obtained from the satellite. On it arrows have been drawn showing the inferred direction of flow. The spiral patterns of flow lines may clearly be seen, and also the presence of a back flow of water around the point and up close to the shore line on the other side, where the silt is then deposited. Looking again at these spirals, isn't it remarkable what Landsat is able to "see" from a distance of over 900 km above the earth. It is evident that soil is being eroded from the east side of Point Pelee, transported around the point and deposited again on the west side. These conclusions have been supported by aerial photography and the whole mechanism of sediment transport has been satisfactorily worked out from measurements of the velocity of flow at various positions in the lake.

Another interesting study of sedimentation was carried out recently in the Bay of Fundy by scientists from the Canada Centre for Remote Sensing, the Virginia Institute of Marine Science and the Bedford Institute of Oceanography. The site had been proposed for a new scheme for the generation of electric power by exploitation of the energy of the tides. It was feared that excessive sedimentation from the tidal barrage might upset the efficient working of the installation. A great deal of data was needed by marine engineers for feeding into mathematical models representing the behaviour of flowing tidal waters and the siltation that might be expected to result.

Before the advent of satellites, data of this sort had to be obtained by moored instruments or by ships which collected water samples for subsequent analysis. This was extremely expensive, and it was possible to sample only a relatively small part of the area, and never the whole at the same time. For a large expanse of water it was not considered feasible. The use of Landsat has enabled us to collect a wealth of data periodically over a long period of time, and the imagery is, moreover, quite cheap. In order to

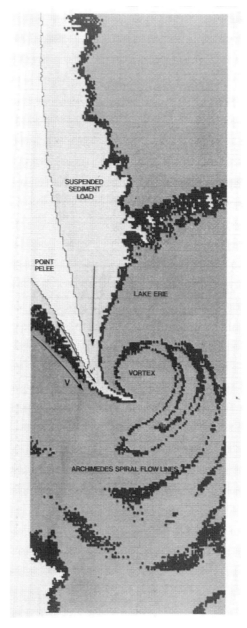

Courtesy of Canada Centre for Inland Waters.

Figure 56. Computer Print-out of Point Pelee.

get a complete story where imagery from different dates can be compared, it is necessary to take account of variations in atmospheric haze, in the angle of the sun's rays (which will be lower in the winter and higher in the summer), in air pollution, sea state and so on.

A new method had recently been implemented at C.C.R.S. based on chromaticity values of Landsat scenes, and the experiment to be described here represented the first time the technique had been used operationally. We might say, therefore, that the study checked not only the behaviour of the waters in the Bay of Fundy, but also the validity of the method itself. Fortunately the method showed itself to be another milestone in the history of remote sensing and proved that it could well be used in operational systems.

First of all, what are chromaticity values?

Physicists have known for a long time that light of one colour can be matched by the suitable mixture of three primary colours. Blue and yellow make green; add a little red and we get brown. These colours and colours in between can be described by saying just how much blue, how much yellow and how much red we used. We then have three numbers representing amounts of three different colours, but we can simplify things a little by saying that we don't really need to know the actual amounts; we need to know only the relative amounts and so we can describe the colour by only two of these values. If, for example, we want to match a colour with 45% blue, 40% yellow and 15% red, we can specify it with any two of these values - say 45% blue and 40% yellow; there is no need to specify the red; it must be 15%. From these values we can derive mathematically so-called chromaticity coordinates, x and y, which can be plotted on a chromaticity diagram.

For the sake of argument we have considered the primary colours to be blue, yellow and red, because that is the way we mix paints; but, in fact, we can use any three primaries we choose provided the colour we wish to describe lies within the gamut of these primaries. We can, if we so choose, use a wavelength outside the visible range, such as in the infrared or ultraviolet. A physicist generally considers the primaries to be blue, green and red. However the chromaticity coordinates, x and y can be calculated and plotted in the same way on a chromaticity diagram. The position of the colour point on the diagram gives information about its dominant wavelength, or hue, and about its purity (i.e. whether it is a clear, pure colour or a muddy colour). The chart does not tell us anything about its brightness, and so the method takes care of one of the variables, i.e. that of atmospheric haze or brightness of the sun. The brightness can be obtained mathematically from another value on the tape. Figure 57 shows a chromaticity diagram.

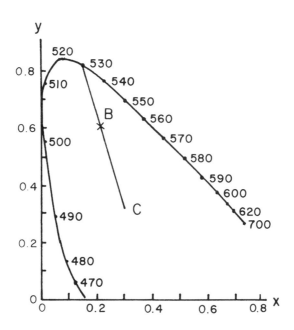

Figure 57. Chromaticity Diagram.

Let us look at an actual case. We will say that ordinary daylight (known by the colour specialists as Illuminant C) is shining on to a surface we wish to describe. The position of C on the diagram is known; it has already been calculated for us by the experts and, as long as we are dealing with daylight conditions, the chromaticity coordinates of the light source will always be x = 0.3101 and y = 0.3163. We will say that we have calculated the chromaticity coordinates of the surface, x and y, to be 0.60 and 0.23 respectively and the plot on the diagram is at B. The figures around the periphery of the curve show the wavelength in nanometres, while the distance of B from C shows the purity expressed as 0 at C and 100% at the periphery. By joinning C to B and continuing to the periphery, we can get information on the colour we are describing. We can see that in this case the dominant wavelength is 530 nanometres, giving a blue-green colour, and the purity is approximately 55%.

As we know, the multispectral scanner of Landsat gives data in the four "colour" bands 4, 5, 6 and 7, representing the colours green, red and 2 infrared bands, 7 being of slightly longer wavelength than 6. We can select any three of these as our primary colours and so use Landsat data directly as a basis for chromaticity calculations. Which bands shall we use? We know that penetration of light into water decreases as the wavelength increases. Therefore, since we want to measure the colour of the water to as great a depth as possible, it is best to use bands 4, 5 and 6. Since the data is recorded digitally on a computer tape, it is already in a very convenient form for computer calculation and for feeding directly into an image analysis system.

Preliminary experiments on lakes and rivers gave a good correlation between Landsat results treated this way and those obtained by measurements on actual water samples collected by boat at the same time as the satellite passed overhead. They showed that chromaticity is directly related to suspended particles, such as sediment, no matter what type and size the particles may be. Results are valid for different days and weather conditions and for different sea states. Due to the wide spectral bands used by the Landsat MSS, it is quite likely that chromaticity calibrations may be extrapolated to different locations (different types of sediment). Current international research is evaluating this exciting possibility. It should also be possible to apply these techniques to the monitoring of biomass, to forestry and to agricultural crops - an interesting and relatively inexpensive procedure. Since the information is already available on tape for all Landsat passes from the day it was launched, we can go back in time and get information from the past. This type of sediment analysis may now be done in a routine fashion at the Canada Centre for Remote Sensing. It is also well suited to a study of ocean dynamics since the pattern of sedimentation across an area shows the way the particles are transported.

In the case of the Bay of Fundy project, it was possible to plug the data into a numerical model which showed that no significant sedimentation problems are likely to arise in connection with the proposed tidal barrage during the lifetime of the project. This was very satisfactory news for its sponsors.

Let us take another example of the applicability of satellite data to coastal water problems. Plate IV shows an image of the Mackenzie Delta area in the Northwest Territories, obtained from Landsat on July 26, 1973 (CCRS ref. no. 10368-20195). The brown areas represent silt and mud carried down to the river mouth. The white blobs represent ice. The water is very shallow here, only about 9 feet deep. An oil company is now building islands and carrying out drilling operations from these. They want to know what environmental changes will be brought about – how the patterns of flow may be changed and how pollution (some of which is inevitable) will affect the area. There is a tremendous amount of wildlife here – seals, polar bears, ducks, etc. Oil-coated waters are anathema to them. Unfortunately if oil is spilt locally on the ice, these darker patches will absorb sunlight more strongly than the surrounding ice; polluted areas will therefore be the first to melt in the Spring, and so it will be to these very spots that the wildlife will flock. The results may well be disastrous to them. When you realise the inaccessibility of these areas for many months of the year it becomes almost frightening. If an oil well blows in the winter, it may have to wait six to eight months before it can be repaired. In the meantime oil would be spewing out into the surrounding areas. The need for us to know more about ice conditions and other such factors becomes imperative. Satellite information is a powerful tool for studying such conditions.

Passing now to ocean waters, colour measurements here are also of value in studying conditions suitable for fish, but for this purpose a different range of wavelengths is required. Pure water looks blue when we look down at it, but, as we know, there is no blue band in the multispectral sensor of Landsat. For a satisfactory analysis of the colour of the sea we need sensors with narrower spectral bands and a better spatial resolution. Mention has already been made in Chapter II of the Optical Multichannel Analyzer which uses a spectrometer in conjunction with 500 detector elements. A somewhat similar instrument was developed for experiments from aircraft on the West coast by scientists from the University of British Columbia and the Institute of Ocean Sciences. It also is in essence a spectrometer whose sensing element is an array of silicon cells. With this it is possible to break the spectrum down into 256 colour components - a considerable improvement over the 4 band spectra of Landsat. A somewhat novel device involving a polarizing filter is able to reduce the spurious effects of light reflected from the top surface layer of the sea. The result is a better spectral resolution except, perhaps, in a rough sea where "clutter" might still be a problem. The spatial resolution is good. At a height of 100 m the instantaneous "foot print" on the sea surface is (1 x 4) m. The instrument collects the data every half-second, during which time the aircraft will have travelled 25 m; since the final reading has a value which is integrated over the half-second time period, the effective size of the foot-print is a track 4 m wide by 25 m long. This compares with a pixel size of Landsat of 57 m x 79 m.

Experiments to test the value of this instrument were carried out by a joint team from the Institute of Ocean Sciences and Seachem Oceanography Ltd. The object was to detect and measure the presence of chlorophyll and simultaneously to measure the temperature of the sea along the southern portion of the British Columbia coast. The chlorophyll content was measured by the spectrometer just described and the temperature was measured by an infrared radiometer. Chlorophyll indicates the phytoplankton content and can be measured in two-ways - by absorption and by fluorescence. Chlorophyll absorbs strongly in the blue part of the spectrum and also in the red; water also absorbs strongly in the red. Therefore water with a low phytoplankton content will appear blue but will become progressively more greenish as the content increases. This "greenishness" may be measured by light collected at 560 nm (green) and at 440 nm (blue). The ratio of the two signals, green to blue, may be taken as a direct measure of the abundance of phytoplankton in the ocean at this point.

Chlorophyll exhibits fluorescence. It re-emits energy at 685 nm (red) which it had previously absorbed at a shorter wavelength, and this shows up as a peak on the reflectance curve. The height of this peak, the fluorescent line height (FLH), also serves as a measure of phytoplankton. This is a relatively new idea which is still undergoing development and it is showing some most interesting results. The method is less sensitive to varying atmospheric and water surface conditions; the reason is partly because red light is less easily absorbed or scattered by haze and other atmospheric conditions than is light of shorter wavelengths, and partly because the fluorescent emission peak is narrow and shows up clearly against the broad-band signals from haze, reflected skylight and whitecaps.

The experiment showed that colour together with thermal infrared data gave a great deal of information on the state of the ocean and its suitability for fish habitats. Sea truth measurements were carried out at the same time by a commercial tug boat belonging to Rivtow Ltd. and the results checked well showing that airborne remote sensing of water colour and temperature may be regarded as an operational method for assessing the quality with regard to phytoplankton content. Results can be immediately communicated to shipping in the area. In the course of the experiment it was noticed that at any point of discontinuity of temperature or colour, fishing vessels appeared to congregate, showing an abundance of fish and thus of phytoplankton. Perhaps a fisherman with a boat is as good at finding fish habitats as is an aircraft armed with a spectrometer!

As already mentioned, Landsat data has been able to give information on colour of the seas. In a later satellite, Nimbus-7, another instrument was incorporated called the Coastal Zone Colour Scanner (CZCS), specially designed for the quantitative determination of chlorophyll and sediment. Like the MSS in Landsat, this is an imaging instrument. It has a better spectral resolution, having 5 bands in the visible range (including the near infrared) and 1 in the thermal infrared range for the measurement of sea surface temperature. The visible bands are designed to detect chlorophyll, sea surface vegetation and "yellow substance", dissolved organic material washed into the sea from land vegetation. The spatial resolution, about 825 m, is not so good as that of Landsat, but for the purposes envisaged this does not matter. It is possible to image a larger area on a smaller scale. The scanner mirror can be tilted on demand from 20° aft to 20° forward in order to avoid sun glint at high sun angles. Like Landsat, Nimbus-7 was placed in a sun-synchronous orbit; it travels 955 m above the earth and crosses the equator at noon each day.

Why are we so interested in the colour of the oceans? As already mentioned colour is related to water quality. It tells us something about the suitability of the locale for fish habitats, and something about pollution and the nature of the pollutants. It also provides data which may be meaningful in a study of oceandynamics. The seas are never still. There are large-scale movements occurring in ocean currents; there is upwelling from the depths of the ocean; there are eddy currents, and the waves themselves promote a mixing and churning of the waters. Colour is one of the factors, which considered together with data from other sources enables a better understanding of the way the sea behaves.

The Gulf Stream is perhaps the most famous of ocean currents, and its effect on climatic and atmospheric conditions has long been recognized. Currents flowing in a north or south direction between the poles and the equator tend to equalize the temperature over these regions and to enable solar energy received at the equator to be transported to colder areas. As we would expect, the boundaries of the Gulf Stream and its direction can be assessed by thermal measurements - by thermometers if used in ships or by infrared scanners if used in aircraft or satellites. The Gulf Stream is also characterized by changes in colour, which as we have just seen can be detected by various instruments from the air and from space.

Extensive studies have been made using data provided by weather satellites, mainly from NOAA satellites executing near-polar, sun-synchronous orbits and from GOES which travels in a geosynchronous orbit. The NOAA satellites with their high resolution thermal imagery collect data twice every 24 hours, once in the day and once at night. Although infrared instruments are able to operate at night, the rays cannot penetrate cloud, and so the measurements are limited to that extent. Nevertheless we managed to gather a great deal of information, both spatial and thermal, and have obtained some exciting results. New pictures of structure have emerged which have never been seen before.

The geosynchronous satellites are only able to provide a lower thermal resolution, but since the data may be collected 40 times a day, there is a better chance of being able to get some good imagery through gaps in the cloud cover.

The Coastal Zone Color Scanner on the Nimbus-7 already mentioned can provide data on colour contrasts across the boundaries of the stream. This may have particular significance for southern regions in the summer months when thermal differences are at a minimum. Research work on this aspect of ocean dynamics is going on at the present time. Already the positions of boundaries for both summer and winter conditions have been traced in great detail from data obtained by research ships and from satellites, and the course of the Gulf Stream has been plotted from the Gulf of Mexico, through the Straits of Florida and off Cape Hatteras. The formation and drift of eddy currents have been seen - cold-core eddies to the south of the stream and warm-core eddies to the north.

These measurements have mostly been made by thermal systems, but more recently Seasat, again moving in a near-polar orbit, has been able to contribute a new kind of data which has proved extremely informative. Mention has already made in Chapter III of some of the results obtained over the sea with the scatterometer. Now we will see some imagery provided by the synthetic aperture radar. As part of the Canadian Sursat programme, imagery was obtained from the satellite and at the same time by aircraft flying immediately below. Whereever possible, measurements were also made at sea level by making use of a ship-of-opportunity. As we have seen, synthetic aperture radar (SAR) is particularly well-suited to the study of textures, and in the case of the sea this means for the study of waves and surface roughness. Seasat was able to measure accurately ocean wavelengths from 100 m to 500 m and also make measurements of wave heights.

Courtesy of MacDonald, Dettwiler and Associates, and Pacific Ocean Sciences Institute.

Figure 58. Radar Image of the Strait of Georgia Taken By Seasat.

Figure 58 shows a Seasat image of the Georgia Strait between Vancouver Island and the mainland. Smooth water appears dark, because when the radar beam strikes a flat horizontal surface it bounces away from the transmitter and is lost. We can see some dark patches in the sheltered bays and coastal areas. The lighter grey areas indicate rougher seas. L-band radar is able to tell us something about the nature and direction of the waves. We can see particularly good imagery of waves when their crests are aligned parallel to the satellite's track. Seasat travels in an approximately north to south direction about 18° off the polar plane. Since the radar beam is directed at right angles to the direction of travel, any surface which is sloping towards the satellite along the track direction will reflect the energy straight back to the receiver. Therefore we see light and dark striations in wave systems which are lined up approximately north and south. On land we can see bright streaks again where the sloping sides of hills and mountains on the islands reflect the beam. About the middle of the picture there is a dark swirl. A little south of this we can just discern an elongated speck, which represents the ship heading north and taking measurements at sea level. The Tsawwassen ferry terminal is at the top and a ferry is crossing to Vancouver, its radar shadow enhancing its visibility. Several other ships are plying the waters between the Gulf Islands. They show up as small white dots caused by the back-scatter of radiation from their metal superstructures; the wakes of the boats are very clear as is particularly evident in the case of a couple of ships in the lower left-hand corner.

Courtesy of Ocean Sciences Institute and SURSAT Project.

Figure 59. Radar Image of the Strait of Georgia Taken By Convair-580.

Figure 59 shows a radar image taken at the same time by the Convair-580 aircraft flying immediately below the satellite. We can now see very clearly the ship which was also taking measurements. The several wave systems in the sea are clearly visible - the smaller crisscross of the capillary waves as well as the larger waves in the other direction which are caused by internal pressures in the sea below. Near the top of the picture there is the darker swirl towards which the ship is moving; this corresponds to the swirl already noted in the radar image and is caused by the tides coming in through Boundary Pass.

It is evident from these pictures that microwave imagery has much to offer the oceanographer in his search for a better understanding of the way the seas behave.

As we have seen elsewhere, the mapping of coastlines from the air and from space now presents few insoluble problems; even small islands and shoals can be accurately located. The measurement of the depth of shallow water is another matter. The urgent requirement for new sources of oil and gas has led to an unprecedented expansion of activity in the Arctic, around Newfoundland and other coastal areas. Hydrographic charts of these areas are at present inadequate, and rapid methods of filling the gaps are needed. Reference has already been made in Chapter II to the lidar bathymeter and its ability to measure the depth of shallow waters and the topography of the seabed.

Field trials have been carried out in several places, including the seas around the Magdalen Islands in the Gulf of the St. Lawrence. This site was particularly good for testing because it provided a wide range of water turbidities, bottom characteristics and sea states. The Quebec government was interested in obtaining accurate measurements of water depths because it was considering the establishment of deep-water ports for salt carriers as well as of commercial shellfish beds in shallow lagoons. The results of these trials were highly successful. The equipment was found to be capable of measuring depths from 0.6 m to 20 m with an uncertainty value of only 0.2 m.

The Canadian Hydrographic Service is at present using this equipment in combination with other techniques such as stereophotometry, photointerpretative hydrography, etc. Photointerpretative hydrography is a quick and cheap planning tool. It is able to make a rapid survey of a region, thus allowing areas to be identified for more detailed work with other instruments. Stereophotometry is another method. Overlapping pictures are taken to provide stereo pairs which can then be looked at through a stereoscope in the usual way. However there are difficulties in the case of open water because there are no landmarks or reference points to serve as a focus for the eye, unless the viewer can make use of a coastline or some other fixed point. The only variation in the scene might be a wave, but by the time the plane has passed on to take the second picture the wave may have moved. Nevertheless it is possible to carry out photogrammetric measurements without fixed targets in the image by using measurement of the aircraft attitude at the moment of exposure. The attitude measurement is made by an inertial navigation system attached rigidly to the aerial camera. An analytical stereoplotter is required to apply this attitude information to the photogrammetric reduction process and to make a correction for the bending of the light rays as they pass through the water surface. Now stereophotometry and lidar bathymetry make an excellent partnership for acquiring quick and accurate data on the seabed of coastal waters. It may be argued that the cost of such equipment and its operation is difficult to justify, since only depths of less than about 20 m can be measured, but these are the areas where most of the accidents occur. Calculations show that of the total waters to be charted about 5% of the area is concerned with depths of less than 10 m; however with conventional sounding methods this relatively small area takes a disproportionately high amount of the budget. If costs could be cut by a factor of 4, this would mean a worthwhile improvement. There is every indication that this could be done. Apart from the cost, there is a question of time. The lidar bathymeter used in conjunction with stereophotography is much faster, and in some areas, such as shallow, ice-infested Arctic waters, it will probably be the only practical solution.

There is no need to tell anyone these days that oil spills are a matter of great concern. There have unfortunately been only too many of them. Anyone who saw the beaches and coastline after the Chedabucto Bay disaster in 1972 must always be aware of the enormity of the problem. That damage was from a small tanker of only 18,000 tons. We now have supertankers of considerably greater tonnage and we are seeing an alarming amount of damage being done to the environment. With the escalation of traffic, accidents are bound to happen, and not only at sea. The heavy traffic in Canada's inland waters, particularly in the Great Lakes area, represents an ever-present hazard. Not all oil spills are accidental. Sometimes ships, against all regulations to the contrary, dump their wastes overboard. Whether the escape of oil is over the sea or over land, the most serious problems occur in the Arctic, partly because it is more difficult to detect the presence of oil in ice-infested waters and partly because, once detected, the situation is more difficult to cope with. The first step in combatting this situation is to be able to detect oil spills as soon as possible after they happen and to delineate their extent as the oil spreads over the water. What help can remote sensing give us in such a situation?

A number of methods are available. Satellite systems have, as always, the undeniable advantage of being able to bring large areas under surveillance at the same time, but, although the presence of slicks has been noted on Landsat imagery, it is difficult to identify the patches positively as oil. The present sensors are not really suited to oil detection, but there is no reason why a future satellite should not carry a sensor specifically designed for this purpose.

As far as the detection of oil is concerned, the most effective weapon without a doubt is the laser fluorosensor as described in Chapter II. It has the ability to discriminate between oils and other substances having a similar appearance and is especially good for use in ice-infested waters - a far more difficult situation than in the open sea. We are assuming, of course, that the oil is present near the surface of the water or ice in a concentration high enough to be detectable. It seems probable that if the amount of oil present is enough to pose a threat to the environment, it will be enough to be detectable. The main disadvantage to the fluorosensor is that it is a line profiler instrument and will not provide us with an image. However if it is used in conjunction with some other imaging sensor, the problem can be overcome.

A suitable combination is a fluorosensor together with an ultraviolet/infrared line scanner. One such scanner, a Daedalus 1230, was used by C.C.R.S. in experiments in the

Arctic. The ultraviolet channel covers the range from 270 nm to 370 nm and the infrared channel from 8.5 μ m to 12.5 μ m. The scanner is able to provide an image in the same way as the multispectral scanner, and to classify oils on water into certain classes such as light (diesel), crude or heavy (bunker fuel). Plate XII shows a colour processed image of an oil spill off Wallop's Island obtained on November 3, 1978. The oil here is classified into thin, thick and thickest oil. We can see that the thin oil, being lighter, spreads more quickly over the sea surface. The ship which allowed the oil to escape appears below and we can trace its passage from the site of the spill by the track of thin oil it has left behind.

Side-looking Airborne Radar has the advantage of being able to cover large areas of the sea very quickly in all weathers, and has been proved by the United States Coast Guard to be extremely useful in detecting small oil slicks resulting from intentional discharges into open waters. Radar systems, as already mentioned, have the ability to differentiate between different textures, and when oil is present the surface of the water is modified (pouring oil on troubled waters?); this produces a recognizable slick. It is not always possible to discriminate between oil slicks, wind slicks or wakes of ships, but it does draw attention to an anomaly which then may be looked at more closely by other methods. It is doubtful, however, whether a microwave technique would be effective on ice or ice-infested seas, but it would be extremely useful in open water and could combine searches for oil spills with other surveillance responsibilities.

A Low-Light Level Television (LLLTV) has much to offer for the detection of oil slicks but it is not able to classify different areas within a slick as to oil thickness, as can be done by the ultraviolet/infrared scanner described above.

These instruments, together with a variety of cameras using both black-and-white and true colour film would offer a powerful tool to the searcher for oil spills. In order to enable the results to be assessed and communicated quickly it would be necessary for the data from all sensors to be brought together and displayed in the aircraft in real-time. This should not pose any very great problem to our design engineers.

Ice, of course, is a special form of water and has its own detection and measurement problems. We have already seen in Plate II a microwave map of the North Pole taken by the satellite Nimbus-5 showing brightness temperatures of ice regions, and in Chapter III we looked at some of the experimental work carried out in connection with the scatterometer. Our experience in remote sensing methods using a wide variety of sensors has now reached the point where it can be usefully applied operationally on a day-to-day basis. Data collected both from the air and from space is now being collected regularly by the Ice Forecasting Central in Ottawa and the information relayed directly to shipping. This, as we can well imagine, is an invaluable service to those responsible for off-shore drilling in northern areas and to fishing and transport ships plying the hazardous waters of the Arctic.

Two long range, 4-engine aircraft are used for ice reconnaissance, concentrating on the Gulf of the St. Lawrence, the St. Lawrence Seaway and the Great Lakes, east Newfoundland and southern Labrador waters, including Lake Melville in winter, with periodic visits to the Arctic. In the summer the southern regions are clear of ice and so the aircraft are moved further north to gather data on the Hudson Bay and Arctic areas.

A number of different sensors are used in these aircraft. A laser profilometer, working on a lidar principle as described in chapter II, provides data on pressure ridges on the ice surface beneath the aircraft. An infrared line scanner measures apparent brightness temperature during ice formation, and an airborne radiation thermometer gives sea surface temperatures. A Side-Looking Airborne Radar records ice conditions during hours of darkness. These rather specialized instruments are supported by a variety of cameras. Each of the aircraft carries a radio facsimile transmitter so that it can pass ice charts immediately to ships and to stations equipped to record them. The information transmitted also includes ice-edge positions, leads and cracks in the ice, ice concentrations and some floe size data, ice pressure features, surface melt and snow cover.

The Ice Forecasting Central, a division of the Atmospheric Environment Service, has been providing information

from aerial reconnaissance for many years. The problem
has been that data from the air is expensive and so
somewhat limited in extent. The advent of satellites and
the possibility of almost daily coverage in northern regions
has meant that a much more detailed and more timely
service can now be provided. The near real-time data
obtainable from Landsat and NOAA satellites has proved
exceedingly useful. Though we may say that, as yet,
satellites are not a primary source of data, they are rapidly
becoming so, and the imagery they provide has become an
integral part of the ice programme. Aerial reconnaissance
is therefore relieved of some of its more routine
responsibilities and is able to provide more support to
Canadian Coast Guard icebreakers in their task of keeping
our northern waters open for shipping as long as possible.
The success of satellite programmes hinges on the
timeliness of the data; information a day old is of little use
to shipping. Methods of communication from Prince Albert
and Shoe Cove have now been developed, and data is relayed
to the Satellite Data Laboratory in Toronto immediately by
means of photofacsimile equipment. Imagery, corrected and
enhanced, is available from Toronto within an hour or two of
the satellites' passing and so can be embodied in daily ice
charts issued by Ice Forecasting Central. Information can
also be obtained on the motion of the ice, which in turn
gives information on oceanographic currents in the Arctic,
knowledge of which is incomplete at the present time. We
can also see something of the rate of growth and decay of
the ice, the degree of roughness and smoothness of the
surface and the age of the ice - all important features in
enabling our ice-breakers to operate more efficiently.

More recently we have seen some extremely interesting
results from aircraft radar, particularly from synthetic
aperture radar carried by the Convair-580; we realize that
the contribution such equipment can make to the solution of
ice problems is without parallel.

Figure 60 shows a radar image obtained by INTERA in
support of a late season oil-drilling operation in October,
1980 by Dome Petroleum Ltd. This was obtained with X-
band radar (3 cm wavelength). Surface roughness is shown
by the relative brightness of the surface. The picture
portrays the ice conditions in the Beaufort Sea over an area

Courtesy of Intera and Dome Petroleum Ltd.

Figure 60. Radar Image of Icefield Taken by Convair-580.

of about 5 km by 3 km and was taken by the synthetic aperture radar aboard the Convair-580. The radar was operating in the X-band and gave a resolution of about 1.6 m. Looking at this we can recognize the superiority of radar for ice imagery. The resolution and detail surpasses anything we have been able to obtain with other methods of measurement. As we have noted before, radar is particularly good at giving information on surface roughness and this accounts for the variations in shades of grey in the picture. Roughness is, in turn, related to the age of the ice. This is an important factor in shipping because multi-year ice is much harder than new ice and so more dangerous. In general because of the presence of brine, sea ice is softer than fresh water ice. Icebergs are pieces of glacier and contain no salt; therefore they are very hard. Multi-year ice has a lower salinity than new ice because over the seasons freezing and thawing have caused much of the salt to be leached out; therefore it is harder. A large piece of multi-year ice can be seen as a light grey mass in the centre of the picture. The black parts represent thin ice with some patches of open water made visible by the wind. Above the central piece of ice can be seen the track of a small ship and we can see that the ship in its voyage wisely avoided the pieces of old ice and followed a path through the thinner and newer ice (blacker). Its track is bright because in its passage the ice was broken up into small chunks. The brighter spot at the top end of its journey shows the ship itself passing through a piece of grey-white ice (10 to 15 cm thick).

Flights such as these are largely experimental at the present time, but they are providing us with experience and knowledge which we hope will later be embodied in the design of radar for satellites. Some results were obtained from Seasat but they were of necessity incomplete; however we are looking forward to the day when we may have a radar satellite dedicated to ice reconnaissance. Considering that synthetic aperture radar has been in use with the civilian remote sensing community only a relatively short time, the imagery we are now getting is quite amazing. As image enhancement and other techniques develop we will be able to realize its full potential. At present the most rewarding results would appear to be in a study of ice conditions.

CHAPTER IX

AGRICULTURE, FORESTRY AND WILDLIFE

As we all know, parts of the world are suffering severe shortages of food because of droughts, floods, storms and disease. Even under ideal conditions we do not grow enough food to support our expanding populations. Satellite information can give us prior warning of unusual shortages and thus give us time to make plans to alleviate their effects, either by more intensive planting in areas where the season is later or by modification of distribution patterns. Remote sensing can offer a great deal of help and information to the agriculturist by assessing the type and magnitude of crops, by monitoring disease and insect infestation, by evaluating the moisture in the soil and earth temperatures and the effects of pollution, weather forecasting, and so on.

The history of air photography for agricultural purposes goes back many years, so that when Landsat was launched in 1972, the experience of the past could be put to good use in analyzing satellite imagery. The advantage of satellites is that crop assessment can be made cheaply and quickly on a global scale. This is particularly valuable to the United States and Canada which supply a large part of the earth's food. It is also useful to the developing countries who at present can get information from the U.S. direct by cooperation with NASA, or through the Food and Agricultural Organization in Rome.

Estimates of crop production depend on three factors - identification of plant species, the acreage under seed and yield. Let us consider identification first. We know that if we look at a field of rice and a field of potatoes we would recognize different shades of green. The colour would also vary according to the maturity of the plants. If we could extend our vision into the near infrared we would be able to recognize much more subtle differences in "colour"; this is the principle behind crop identification. Each type of vegetation has its own spectral signature. It remains for us to learn how to detect and to interpret it. A great deal of

work has been done and is being done on spectroradiometric
curves relating to a variety of plants; while not every kind
of vegetation can yet be identified by such curves alone,
progress along these lines is being made; by combining
spectral records with other information such as time of the
year, maturity of plants, and where possible a classification
key from ground-based data, a great deal of knowledge can
be gained. Work has been carried out in the United States
on the use of satellite data for the identification of corn and
soybeans in South Dakota, Illinois and Michigan, field corn
and popcorn in Nebraska, winter wheat in Kansas, rice,
safflower, asparagus, corn and cotton in California.
Research at Purdue University has shown that it is possible
to obtain spectral signatures from airborne sensors for the
identification of several crop species including wheat, oats,
corn, soybeans, alfalfa, red clover and rye. In Canada the
Research Branch of Agriculture Canada has carried out
experiments in Saskatchewan which show good correlation
of satellite and aerial data with ground records for rapeseed
and cereal crops. Experiments in New Brunswick have
resulted in an operational method for the detection of
potato crops, which will be discussed later.

When it comes to the second factor in estimating crop
production - that of acreage, satellite data can be readily
used for large areas, and of course these are the most
important, but for smaller areas it is necessary to
supplement the data by the use of aircraft. Satellite images
are not much good for looking at individual fields as the
resolution is not good enough, although computer methods
involving both aircraft and satellite are being worked out

Good yields depend on healthy crops. In the assessment
of yield and the monitoring of disease remote sensing serves
a real need. We think we can see by eye when a plant is
healthy; we note the change in colour of the leaves, but by
that time the disease is far advanced.

Colour-infrared photography may detect this condition
before we can see it for ourselves, when there may still be
time to do something about it. By means of satellite
imagery we may be able to plot the large-scale progress of
the disease across fields even countries, and perhaps be able
to stop it before it gets out of hand. Aerial photography
will give information on a more detailed scale as may be

seen in Plate VIII. This is a colour-infrared aerial photograph of experimental potato plots which had been deliberately infected with late blight. The diseased plants, bluish in colour, show up very clearly against the magenta background of healthy plants. Diseases in beans and potatoes are easily detected from the air because the diseased leaves are generally on top. Rust in wheat is not quite so easy because the diseased leaves are underneath. Most conditions of stress can be spotted at an early stage whether they be due to drought, disease, or insects. The key to this identification is the difference in infrared reflectance of healthy plants and those under stress.

Let us consider what happens when sunlight falls on a leaf. Sunlight from a clear sky contains visible light (all colours of the rainbow from violet to red) and a broad spectrum of invisible rays as, for example, ultraviolet and infrared radiation. Of the visible bands the plant utilizes the blue and red to synthesize starches and sugars; the green light it does not need; some of this passes through the leaves to the ground below and some is thrown back into the air again, or reflected, and so we see a leaf as green in colour. The largest part of the sun's energy is in the infrared region; fortunately the plant does not absorb rays of these wavelengths, otherwise the whole system would become very warm and we would lose the cooling effect of trees and grass that we enjoy in the summer. A healthy plant reflects nearly all the near infrared energy it receives, and though we cannot see these wavelengths, they are detectable by infrared film in a camera, or by the Landsat multispectral scanner. If on the other hand a plant is not healthy, its infrared reflectance is drastically reduced. This change in infrared reflectance serves as a warning to the agriculturist that all is not well with his crops. It is interesting to note that while the invisible infrared reflectance of a dying leaf is decreased, the visible red reflectance is increased since the plant can no longer use it for photosynthesis. This is why leaves turn red in the Fall.

The monitoring of plant diseases is of tremendous economic as well as sociologic importance throughout the world. In the United States, for example, it is estimated that average annual losses caused by insects and disease amount to about $20 billion. In developing countries losses are relatively even higher and may have devastating effects on the population. The desert locust causes millions of dollars of damage every year in Africa and the Middle East. There are bad seasons in Canada when our wheat crops may be attacked by rust, aphids may infect our corn, and blight may devastate our bean and potato crops, causing considerable damage and financial loss. In southwestern Ontario, for example, the white bean growers produce a crop worth about $40 million annually. Bacterial blight, which can easily be detected at an early stage by colour-infrared photography, can cause losses in yield of up to 40%. While detection of the onslaught of disease is not a cure, it is the first stage in tackling the problem and should be the means of bringing about high levels of production.

Another advantage of satellite imagery is the rapidity with which we can obtain and analyze the data. This is a very important factor for agricultural managers. Assessment is of no use when the season is over, except for statistical purposes for the subsequent years. At present there are some disadvantages because data can be collected only once every 18 days, but this situation will be improved when we have more satellites with staggered orbital dates.

The possibility of using remote sensing for the detection of alfalfa sickness in crops was investigated by scientists from the Department of Soil Science at the University of Alberta under a project sponsored by the Alberta Remote Sensing Center. Alfalfa is an important crop commercially, and interruption of supplies in the harvesting season is of great concern to the processing industry. Methods for the early detection of alfalfa sickness were therefore sought.

An experiment was carried out on a site near the town of Mallaig, northeast of Edmonton. Images from both aircraft and satellite were studied and compared. It was found that colour-infrared photography from the air offered the best promise for the differentiation between sick and healthy plants. Landsat images were found to be not too satisfactory because of their small scale, but better assessment could probably be made by the use of digital data.

A reliable estimate of any crop before it is harvested would be of great assitance to industry, particularly the food processing companies, and to government agricultural departments, who would then be able to plan efficient handling and marketing operations.

Statistics Canada is very interested in getting timely, accurate estimates of potato and canola-rapeseed crops – both commodities of great economic importance to Canada. The production of potatoes is a particularly important factor in the economy of both Prince Edward Island and New Brunswick. In the past, in order to evaluate the crop acreage, governments sent out questionnaires to the farmers; the replies were supplemented by personal interviews of a random selection of farmers, and all the data combined to arrive at an estimate of the annual production. This was a time-consuming task; the results were not too reliable and it was never possible to get the figures early enough to be of much use for the current year's planning.

Potato plants grow close to the ground and their leaves form a dense canopy over the soil. This suggests that spectral signatures of these plants from air or from space would be very well defined. Some work was carried out along these lines by scientists from the Canada Centre for Remote Sensing in 1975 and they showed that it was possible to separate potatoes from other crops with a high degree of accuracy. Consequently Statistics Canada asked C.C.R.S. to cooperate with them in studying the possibility of devising an operational method using remote sensing methods for the forecasting of crop production. Experiments were carried out in the Upper St. John River area using both satellite imagery and high altitude normal colour photography. For the satellite work, computer compatible tapes corrected by the Digital Image Correction System were analyzed by the C.C.R.S. Image Analysis System. Two main problems were encountered. One was the proper classification of boundary pixels, which might contain in part potatoes and in part some other crop. This would lead to errors which would be relatively greater in small fields where the ratio of perimeter to total area would be greater. The problem was partially overcome by mathematical calculation and subsequent modification of the boundaries. The second problem concerned other crops, such as peas, whose spectral signature could be confused with that of potatoes. However peas are generally harvested by mid to late August, and so by collecting the data on potatoes later in the season this confusion could be eliminated. Another fact to be borne in mind is that if the cloud cover is excessive, a back-up arrangement for survey from the air might be needed.

The results of the 1980 project confirmed the early finding. Two different methods of calculation were used by C.C.R.S.; one gave the total acreage in the whole of New Brunswick to be 51,524 and the other a figure of 51,119. The area as published by Statistics Canada was 52,000 acres. The results were therefore within the 85% accuracy which was asked for. Less than four hours of time on the image analysis system were required to perform the area estimate for the entire potato belt, and the whole project was completed within the time prescribed. As a result of this quite outstanding success Statistics Canada is planning to adopt satellite imagery together with some traditional procedures as an operational method for the evaluation of potato acreage; they are setting up arrangements for training some of their personnel in remote sensing methods. They are also considering the use of satellite monitoring processes for other crops, and work is now underway to assess its value for rapeseed – an important crop in Alberta.

Of course, acreage is only one factor in determining the total production of a crop. The soil and the weather are others.

Perhaps the most positive information that remote sensing can give us on soils, concerns its moisture content and factors affecting it, such as the whereabouts of fresh water, the rates of snow melt in the spring and forecasts of the amount of water available for irrigation. Thermal infrared scanning has proved particularly good for this purpose, as already discussed in the last chapter; for sufficiently large bodies of water detection by satellite is also effective. For example, a farmer would like to have information on unexpected leakages of water from his irrigation channels, and variations that may occur in the soil as a water course changes position, or a river is diverted into another channel. There is evidence that, over the past few years, the weather patterns of the world are shifting. The Sahara desert has appeared to be moving further south in response to these changes with the result that vast areas of grassland in Northern Nigeria are drying up; the remaining areas are being severely overgrazed giving rise to widespread starvation. These changing positions can now be seen by satellite imagery, but it is too late. Had Landsat been up two or three years earlier, we would have had some warning. Admittedly nothing could have been done to prevent the Sahara from shifting any more than Canute could have stopped the tides, but it might have been possible to shift the population or make some plans for providing them with alternative sources of food.

Western Canada has a problem with solonetzic soils. These are soils with a high salt content and they generally give rise to poor crops. Since about 15 to 20 million acres in the settled areas are involved, this has become a matter of some concern. Attempts have been made to combat the problem by a deep-plowing technique, and a method was needed to assess the efficacy of this procedure. The Alberta Remote Sensing Centre therefore sponsored a study of suitable remote sensing methods, and experiments were carried out by scientists from the Department of Soil Science at the University of Alberta, Edmonton. Sites were selected from a number to which the Soils Branch, Alberta Agriculture, had applied deep-plowing treatments. Of the several airborne techniques investigated the most successful were found to be colour and colour-infrared photographs. These were semi-oblique aerial photographs taken with a hand-held camera, and the results showed that the deeply plowed plots had more uniform plant growth and the yields were considerably higher.

Plate XIII shows colour and colour-infrared photographs of a test site taken on two different dates - July 18 and August 17, 1977. The area had been seeded with rapeseed, and by mid-July it was in bloom, which accounts for the yellowish hue of the colour photograph (upper left). The colour-infrared photographs (right hand side of Plate XIII) shows that this is a very effective technique for showing up the difference in poor and healthy crops. The red coloration shows areas of good crop growth and good ground cover on non-saline soils, while the purplish colour shows poor growth and poor ground cover on saline soils.

Comparative quantitative estimates of the treated and untreated areas were not made, but qualitative examination showed that there was good correlation between the colour on the image and the crop yields as measured on the ground.

It is obviously a good way of judging the effect of deep-plowing and the uniformity or otherwise of the distribution of salt in the soil.

Everyone knows the dependence of the farmer on the weather. Here again we can get some assistance from the satellites. The weather satellites, Tiros, Nimbus and NOAA, have revolutionized the science of forecasting. While they are not able to do anything about controlling the weather they can tell us beforehand what it is likely to be. Progress is being made in forecasting weather patterns for longer periods of time. This information is invaluable to a farmer in his planning; he will know what is the best time to plant and harvest his crops, when he should protect his fruit trees from frost, and when he should bring his cattle into the barns in the Fall, or let them out in the Spring. These represent positive economic gains which are currently being derived from space research. Since weather is such an important factor in crop production, the data from weather satellites can be used for plugging directly into mathematical models of crop estimates.

In 1973 the United States launched a programme called LACIE, which stands for Large Area Crop Inventory Experiment. Its aim was to develop a remote sensing method for the annual forecasting of wheat crops over the whole world. Wheat was chosen because it is a major crop in world markets and is grown in many different geographical areas and so is subjected to different climatic conditions. There were some complications; the spectral signatures of wheat vary slightly from one part of the world to another, and they may be confused with the spectral signatures of other crops, especially other cereal crops. As in the case of the potato crop, it is desirable for the experimenter to know something of the harvesting procedures of the wheat crop and also of other crops with which it might be confused. Canada assisted in this study; with her large acreage of wheat she was able to contribute much meaningful data at different times of the year. The data from Landsat was analyzed in the early stages of crop development and the results fed into a mathematical model together with climatological and meteorological data, as well as any other data obtainable from conventional data sources. The results were very rewarding. It is now possible to forecast results which are within 15% of production for each country 90% of the time. The experiment proved that the method was suitable for the world-wide monitoring of wheat crops; it is now being used operationally and is being extended to the estimate of other crops such as soyabeans, corn, etc.. This is obviously one of the great benefits bestowed by satellite imagery and is likely to prove of particular value to the developing countries.

These happy results led to the development of the thematic mapper already mentioned in Chapter IV. The thematic mapper was planned with agricultural applications in mind. Its ability to accept signals from the earth in seven wavelength bands, chosen for their significance to vegetation, and to classify the data received to produce a thematic map will make it invaluable for agricultural identification. Change detection techniques will allow the development of crops to be watched throughout the growing season. Agricultural management on a global scale will thus be possible - something which we hope will enable us to fight the battle against starvation and want for millions of people.

A somewhat different type of problem is the assessment of rangelands used for feeding cattle. Alberta, for example, contains large areas of government land - 26 million hectares in south Alberta alone - which are leased out to independent ranchers, who are responsible for the condition and inspection of them. Altogether there are about 90 leases, some of which are as big as 16,000 to 24,000 hectares. A range manager may have 9 or 10 or these under his jurisdiction. Hitherto the grazing lands have been regularly inspected to check that they are being properly managed. This has been carried out largely by ground survey crews - an expensive and time-consuming task. We might expect that satellite technology would have some application under such conditions. Accordingly a study was made in 1980 by a team of scientists from the Canada Centre for Remote Sensing, the Lands Division of Alberta Energy and Natural Resources and the Alberta Remote Sensing Center to see to what extent Landsat imagery might assist in the mammoth job of monitoring the mixed grass rangelands of the Province.

Plate XIV is an example of imagery from a Landsat

scene that has been suitably enhanced. The interpretation of such an image requires a good deal of experience because the colour values will vary considerably throughout the year, and different grasses may appear darker than others. In this image the black areas indicate water; the blue coloration shows grazing land. The lighter tones correspond to ranges with less biomass; this may have been brought about by overgrazing or by poor growth conditions. The darker areas correspond to good range conditions; here there is a lot of brown biomass present mixed in with the green, which would indicate that the area had been undergrazed. In such places there would be a higher proportion of seed to carry over to the next year and the presence of the dead vegetation would improve the productivity of the soil. This would bode well for the next year's crop. In general, pinkish coloration shows poor rangelands.

It is easy to see that such information can be of great assistance in showing a range manager areas that may be underutilized. Thus he will be able to plan in advance for the better disposition of his cattle for the future. He can see where he may need to make more water available by, perhaps, using a bulldozer to dig deep trenches into which the water may flow and collect.

The results of the whole study have been extremely rewarding. One range manager near Medicine Hat, where the areas are particularly large, estimated that it would normally take him 3 weeks to carry out an inspection of one of his leases, but with a Landsat map it would take him only 2 to 3 days. Whereas, previously he would expect to visit and survey each lease only once every 2 or 3 years, he can now receive a set of images such as those in Plate XIV once a year; he is thus able to keep a continuous watch on conditions, and can organize his visits more profitably in terms of time.

The foresters were among the first people to appreciate the value of remote sensing; this is not surprising when we consider how remote and often inaccessible are some of our timber stands. In the past the reserves of timber in Canada have been so enormous for such a relatively small number of people that we have become careless in our use of trees; we may justly be accused of squandering our resources with little thought of the morrow. This situation is rapidly changing. The population is increasing and is becoming more aware of the fact that the forest resource is not boundless. It is claimed that the quantity of paper per capita used by a nation is an index of its level of education, and more paper used means more trees destroyed. With increased wealth there is a greater demand for lumber for housing and other consumer products. With more leisure time and with a greater concentration of the people in urban centres there is a greater demand for recreational areas in the forest, and wildlife requires the protection given by the woods.

These competing claims to forest land have to be taken into consideration, and forest management has assumed a new importance. In order to plan effectively we need up-to-date information on the amount of wood available, its location, its type, its health and its accessibility. It is feasible to get this information on the scale necessary only by using remote-sensing methods. Both airborne and space systems play their part. Airborne equipment is able to give information on individual trees and can cover large areas fairly quickly. Satellite imagery with its repetitive, overall view can monitor the forest areas even more quickly over a much wider area, but not in so much detail. The two methods are complementary to each other and to ground survey measurements.

Early work depended almost entirely on ground survey measurements. These were costly and time-consuming and quite impossible to carry out over large areas and in inaccessible places. Timber cruisers were able to take measurements only at the periphery of a forest or along water courses where access was possible. Despite the increasing use of snowmobiles and helicopters large areas of wooded lands remained out of reach. Research in mensuration was therefore undertaken to develop new techniques to reduce the amount of field work necessary. This has mostly evolved around small-and medium-scale aerial photography. In the first place large-scale photographs are obtained of randomly selected plots within the area to be assessed. The key to success lies in the wise selection of plots to ensure that they are representative of the whole. The photographs are examined closely to identify the species of individual trees; certain characteristic features of the tree, such as height, crown shape and size, degree of compactness and texture can be measured and classified. These characteristics in turn can be used to estimate the diameter and wood volume of the trees - the features of greatest value in deciding how a forest may best be used and managed. A considerable amount of help can be given by studying stereoscopic pairs of photographs. Aerial photographs, even of so small a size as a 70 mm film, permit the identification of tree species and, if the scale is sufficiently large, even the description of individual trees. Measurements are made on a large scale photograph of crown area as a guide to the volume of wood. In order to relate measurements on the photograph to measurements on the ground it is necessary to know the focal length of the camera lens and the height of the aircraft above ground. A radar altimeter developed by the National Research Council of Canada in cooperation with the Forest Management Institute provides a simple, rapid and convenient method for measuring this altitude. The altitude may be read directly on a meter and automatically recorded on the edge of the photograph being taken. Thus the photographs, taken with a 60% overlap and viewed stereoscopically, can yield information on the location, quantity and types of trees. This method of forest inventory, developed by the Forestry Management Institute will likely be used operationally in many parts of the world, although it is being partly replaced by satellite imagery.

Trials carried out in Quebec by the Quebec Department of Lands and Forests over one-tenth acre plots in black spruce-fir stands have been eminently successful. The total census of merchantable timber as derived from the photographs was only slightly below that obtained from ground measurements. Subsequent developments have led to even more accurate estimates. As a result of these preliminary tests an inventory programme covering the almost 100,000,000 hectares of Quebec's forest land was carried out - a programme which would not have been conceivable before the advent of remote sensing.

Satellite imagery has much to offer in the assessment of forest areas and in the classification of types of trees. As an example we will take a further look at Plate III of the Montreal and Ottawa area. On it is drawn a square depicting the Larose Forest area about 30 miles east of Ottawa. It represents about 1/36 of the whole area and comprises 216,000 pixels. An experiment was carried out on this region by the Forest Management Institute, Ottawa. Using data from computer compatible tapes they produced with the cooperation of Computing Devices of Canada a thematic map showing forests, agricultural areas, etc. We have already seen in Chapter VII an interpretation of the picture as a whole; we saw how large geographic features have been given a new expression by means of these small-scale overviews of a large area. Now we will take the small area enclosed in the square and see how much more detail can be extracted from the Landsat tape. The Larose area was known to contain plantations about 35 years old consisting of white spruce, red pine, white pine and poplar. Using a computer compatible tape the computer was able to distinguish seven ground classes (i.e. it recognized seven spectral signatures). It was then necessary to "train" the computer to tell us what these spectral signatures represented. You remember that in order to do this we need to have some ground truth. This ground truth data was gathered from a training area which covered about one percent of the whole test area. It was obtained by a study of forest cover maps, supplemented by field checks, and by medium- and small-scale colour and colour-infrared aerial photographs. By knowing the content of small sample areas (taken pixel by pixel) within the training area, we were able to ask the computer to survey the whole of the Larose Forest area and to print out a thematic map using letters to represent the different ground classes, viz: A - Agricultural land, C - Coniferous forest, D - Deciduous forest, W - Water, M - Bare soil and muddy water, U -Unknown. A portion of this map is shown in Figure 61. Outlines have been drawn around each separate class of material so that they may be recognized more easily. Of particular interest is the water and mud marked W and M. This records the landslide that took place into the South Nation River in May, 1971, and shows the higher water levels upstream from the slide.

The magnetic tape containing the classification data for this map was also used in an image recorder to produce a coloured thematic map printed on photographic film as shown in Plate VI. Here the ground classes were printed in different colours.

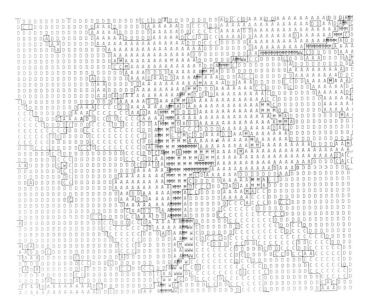

Courtesy of Forest Management Institute Forestry Service.

Figure 61. Computer Print-out of Larose Forest Area.

These maps are all multispectral maps with data taken from all four bands of the multispectral scanner. All the values were taken from the satellite record obtained on a single date, September 5, 1972. Analysis of the results showed that the accuracy of thematic mapping was good, about 80% of the pixels being classified correctly. The experiment demonstrated quite clearly the feasibility and advantage of using computers to produce thematic maps directly from Landsat digital data recorded on computer compatible tapes. However we would still like to improve the accuracy. In an attempt to do this, records were taken of satellite passes on three different dates (September, 1972, March, 1973 and October, 1973) and the data combined to give a multispectral, multidate image. The thinking behind this idea was that by doing so we would average out discrepancies due to seasonal changes and other small errors that might cause a misrepresentation of the data. This indeed proved to be the case and a classification accuracy of 83% was achieved. This, I think you will agree, is remarkably good considering that the accuracy was calculated from vegetation classes whose spectral signatures are quite similar. A much higher accuracy could be expected if we were to distinguish between objects with very different spectral signatures. The computer printout of this combined imagery is shown in Plate VII. After print-out, it was coloured by hand to allow the areas to be more easily recognized.

This particular experiment was carried out several years ago but it is still important because it was one of the first of such procedures on which others have been based. Modern image analysis systems have improved and are capable of classification into a greater number of classes. Digital image correction systems now provide more accurate geographical location and, equally important, the expertise of the interpreter has improved with experience. All of these things have led to improved accuracy and greater confidence on the part of the user in remote sensing techniques.

It is evident then that both airborne and spaceborne instruments have much to offer the forest manager in the assessment and planning of his timber resources.

Many of the provinces are now making use of a combination of airborne and spaceborne methods for inventory purposes. B.C., for example, with a forest area of approximately 52,000,000 hectares is now using satellite imagery on an operational basis. It cost them about 10 to 15 million dollars over a 15-year period to obtain a complete inventory by using vertical photographs on panchromatic and colour film carried by aircraft and helicopter. They are now looking for the quickest and cheapest way of keeping the resulting maps up-to-date. Much of the timber in the forests is sold to industrial companies, and checks must continually be made to ensure that these companies are, in fact, logging on the areas allotted to them. Landsat RBV and MSS products are being used to monitor depletions and to map clearcut areas in those regions where recent conventional aerial photography is not available.

Landsat MSS data in digital form is analyzed on the

image analysis system. Radiometric and geometric corrections are carried out, and then a change detection method is applied using computer tapes from different dates. The depletion boundaries may be inscribed and the actual area given without the need for additional computations. This is going to mean a further saving of time and money for the Inventory Branch. Considering that they have at present over 7,000 maps, the total savings will be considerable.

Another type of forest map is the forest fuel map – an invaluable asset when a fire breaks out. In the early days of satellite operation it was argued that the maps derived from satellite data were not sufficiently detailed and did not present the data in a form that could be readily understood by fire-control personnel. However, recently developed methods of image enhancement and presentation are now providing an acceptable format. They are currently being used by the initial attack dispatchers who decide how much force to dispatch to each fire. If the fire is in hardwoods it will probably be easy to stop. If it is in young conifer – send 2 airtankers and a helicopter ! We might say that in no other operation is immediacy of such importance. Faced with raging forest fires over large areas, such as happened in Northern Ontario in the summer of 1980, every single item of information must be used and used quickly. There is no time under these conditions to start drawing maps; they must be ready and up-to-date before hand. Remote sensing methods play an important part both in preparing the maps in the first place and revising them at frequent intervals afterwards. First and foremost a forest fuel map will give a picture of types of fuel in the path of the fire. Coniferous trees are a more dangerous fuel than deciduous trees. Dead and dying trees as a result of windstorms, or heavy insect damage in pure stands of conifer are particularly hazardous and these can be shown clearly on a fire fuel map. The maps should also show the location of logging and access roads which would enable men and supplies to reach the site of the fire in the shortest possible time; of natural or man-made fuel breaks; and of tiny lakes and ponds suitable for use by the pump crews. The current maps show the large lakes suitable for airtankers, but in most of Canada's forests the main tool for fire control is the water pump and ground crew; the position of the smaller bodies of water would be useful knowledge. Scientists from the Forest Fire Research Institute of Environment Canada set about devising quick methods of providing suitable pictures. They were assisted by others from the Canada Centre for Remote Sensing, the Department of National Defence (Defence and Civil Institute of Environmental Medicine) and Plate XV shows the result of their endeavours. It is about 1/16 of a standard Landsat picture and is printed here at a scale of 1:150,000. It would be photographically enlarged to a scale of 1:80,000 for operational use by the forest fire control centre. It represents the area around Hook Lake in Quebec, here circled in white. Water bodies are shown in black (W); recent clearcut areas are shown in red (R), while older ones are in yellow (O). Light green areas (H) depict mixed hardwoods with lighter yellow-green tones indicating pure stands. Blue-grey areas (S) show mixed softwood with darker areas indicating pure stands. A map such as this assists in communication during the course of a fire between aircraft or helicopter personnel and ground crews; it also serves as a base reference which can be added to as the fire progresses and data arrives at the control room from workers on the ground or in the air. This together with data on windspeeds and direction, location of crew, etc. enables the fire boss to deploy his men and equipment to the best advantage.

The Société de Conservation de l'Outaouais (SCO) has been among the leaders in applying techniques such as these to fire-fighting. It is responsible for protecting one of the largest and most valuable forest regions in Quebec, and yet by using modern methods including fire maps obtained from satellite data it is able to operate with the smallest permanent staff and the smallest budget. Traditionally fire maps, when used at all, have been prepared by hand-coloring drawings derived from inventory maps, but these take a considerable amount of time and consequently are prohibitively expensive for large-scale use. Using prints from Landsat data enabled the entire Outaouais fire control region to be mapped in less than two person-weeks and only cost about $5,000. Since that time the maps have been updated twice with very little trouble and expense. These have now been in use since 1975 at the Fire Control Centre and initial costs have been recovered many times over. We might say that there are three stages in the overall operation of fire-fighting. First of all we must detect the fire promptly when it is at a stage where it can be easily and inexpensively controlled. Secondly, we must have an efficient organization of men and equipment ready to go into action. If the initial attack fails, a large fire will probably result. At this time a "campaign" fire organization will be set up, involving large numbers of men and equipment. We must therefore have a programme which will allow the fire boss to be informed of the location of the fire boundaries, and the speed of propagation and also of local hot spots. Thirdly there is the mopping-up operation afterwards to ensure that no smouldering fires remain either above or below the ground, which might later come to life again with a gusting wind. While a fire is raging, the whole area is engulfed in smoke; crews on the ground find it impossible to see what is going on. Those flying overhead in aircraft or helicopter are unable to see much but smoke and flames, and visual methods of remote sensing are useless. Thermal infrared techniques with their ability to penetrate smoke and haze are the obvious answer, and most Canadian provinces now utilize some form of infrared detection as part of their fire-fighting tool kit.

Two of the simpler instruments are the Hughes Probeye and the AGA Thermovision, which are particularly suitable for detecting fires over small areas and for mopping-up operations afterwards. One of the problems of great concern to the Government of British Columbia is that of "hang-over" fires from the burning of slash in the cut-over areas of the forests. This burning is generally done in the fall, and local hot spots can persist through the winter only to flare into life again in the following spring or summer. They are often smokeless and so escape visual detection by airborne patrols. The Pacific Forest Research Centre in Victoria therefore carried out experiments in the Cariboo and Kamloops Forest Districts in order to assess the value of the AGA instrument for early detection. This is an imaging system which portrays the scene below in real time on a cathode ray tube. It may be mounted on an aircraft or a helicopter. A helicopter was found to be more satisfactory because it can fly at a lower height and more slowly, and it is better able to manoeuver in tight turns. An analysis of the survey results showed many potential fire sources that would otherwise have escaped detection.

The Probeye is an even simpler type of instrument; it is less sensitive, but is yet sensitive enough if used at night or in the early hours of the morning when the ground is at its coolest. It is only about one-third to one-quarter the price of the Thermovision unit, and so we can afford to keep more of them in operation. They are widely used across the country on a routine basis. The B.C. Government, for example, is using 16 Probeye detectors - one in each of its forest fire divisions - and one Thermovision instrument which is centrally located. Every spring an aircraft or helicopter carrying a Probeye unit flies over several thousand prescribed log-burning areas to check the fire situation before the summer begins. It is expected that by the use of such measures we will be able to save many millions of dollars annually by putting out fires before they get away, and this is the best time for combatting a fire.

Although this is an admirable system for fire detection and mopping-up operations, it is inadequate for large fires. Here a somewhat more sophisticated arrangement is required, such as an infrared line scanner with its larger angle of view.

Intertech Remote Systems Ltd. are using such a system and are providing its services to control agencies all over the country. The actual infrared unit, the firemapper, works on the principle outlined in Chapter III. The output from the detector goes through a control box which splits the signal into two parts. One half goes to a recorder and the other half goes to a printer which provides an image of the scene below. The lapse time between its reception by the detector and the print-out of the final image is only 15 to 20 seconds; so we might say it is almost real time. The paper on which the scene is printed is put into a plastic container and dropped through a hole in the floor of the aircraft to the fire camp below. The fire boss is thus able to get a picture in minutes of just where the boundaries of the fire are, where the hottest part of it is, and whether there are any spots where the fire, supposedly extinguished, has flared up again. This is a tremendous advance over earlier methods of fire-fighting which left the crews virtually in the dark, merely able to guess at what was going on. Further development work is continuing in which a direct communication link will be provided to earth; the original output from the detector will then be divided into three parts – the two parts already referred to and a third which will be telemetered directly to the fire boss.

The whole fire mapping system now consists of a twin-engine aircraft carrying the firemapper and a 3-man crew – the pilot, the scanner technician and the mission manager. It also carried a special navigation system which is programmed for flying accurate flight lines in smoke or at night in remote areas.

There are basically two types of operation for which the system is suitable. First, there is the daylight mission for active fire-mapping from a height of about 8,000 ft. to 10,000 ft. – particularly attractive when a fire is travelling rapidly. A fire can move at about 25 feet per second, which is faster than man can run. The picture received on the ground will show just how close to a town the fire front may be and what roads are available, if evacuation should be necessary. Secondly, there is the nighttime mission for detecting hot spots, generally flown at a lower height of about 2,000 ft. to 3,000 ft. in order to get sufficient detail. These hot spots are frequently not very hot and might be confused with rocks warmed by the sun if they were registered in the day.

We can see that fortunately for us a new generation of firefighters is coming into existence and their knowledge and expertise will not only make fire-fighting less hazardous, but also more effective. Remote sensing methods play a very important role in the whole process. They assist in the production of fuel maps before a fire starts; they assist in the detection of fires in the first place, in the management of the fire-fighting operation when an active fire is raging, and in the mop-up operation when it is over. Finally when the last battle against the elements has been won, remote sensing is able to assess the damage. Change detection techniques using satellite imagery are able to show the area that has been destroyed, and this in turn is of assistance to insurance companies or government departments against whom claims may be made.

These new techniques may be foreign to some of our

existing fire managers and an education process may be necessary. Such programmes are being offered in several provinces. For example, Intertech Remote Sensing Ltd. is setting up courses for fire control agencies. The Ontario Centre for Remote sensing provides training in the practical application of thermography to a number of fields as part of a major technology transfer programme. The Alberta Remote Sensing Center is also carrying out educational programmes along these lines.

So much for the present. What of the future? Development is now continuing in the use of greatly improved line scanners for the detection of fires. Small fires of only several square feet in size can be detected through thick forests from an altitude of 20,000 feet, day or night. At such altitudes it is possible to cover a considerable area of ground in a single flight, which makes the exercise a more economical proposition. Also research indicates that there is promise in the application of passive microwave techniques to fire detection. Fires emit considerable amounts of microwave radiation that can penetrate dry vegetation; this should make it theoretically possible to map deep-burning peat fires, where infrared methods now fail. Perhaps it is not too much to hope that the blackened areas we see so frequently as we journey through our forest regions will soon be a thing of the past. Certainly the enormous financial loss experienced in Canada every year warrants the expenditure of a considerable amount of money if such fires can be prevented.

As already mentioned in Chapter III, infrared imagery can be used effectively for the detection of temperature differences at the low end of the scale as well as at the high end. This makes it useful for the location of frost pockets. On spring nights when skies are clear and air temperatures only a little above freezing point, there is a risk of frost in low-lying areas, particularly in small hollows in the terrain. Heat radiated from the ground to the sky above creates a layer of colder air in contact with the ground. This cooler air being a little heavier than the rest, flows downhill into these hollows, and although the air temperature may be a little below 5°C, the ground temperature may be down to -1°C or less. Local cold spots can play havoc with newly planted seedlings. Most forest damage occurs in the late spring when the growing season is at its height. The newly-grown shoots are tender and have high water content; this makes them very susceptible to frost damage. Repeated freezing may destroy the plant. Even if it is not totally destroyed, the plant is weakened and becomes prey to many forms of bacteria.

Research work carried out by the Ontario Centre for Remote Sensing in cooperation with the School of Forestry at Lakehead University, Thunder Bay, sought to study site factors involved in the formation of frost pockets in forest cut-over areas. The areas were mapped by thermography, which proved to contain useful information in planning reforestation measures. The fruit growers in the Okanagan Valley are also interested in these techniques and further work is now being done to find out to what extent fore-knowledge of frost-prone areas would be able to save the growers some of the considerable losses they experience each year from their apple, peach and grape crops.

Fire and frost are not the only hazards a tree faces in its lifetime. As in the case of other forms of vegetation, remote sensing is able to give us a great deal of information about the health of a tree. Damage due to insects, disease, air pollution (particularly sulphur dioxide fumes) and excess or lack of water may be recognized on aerial photographs using colour-infrared film. Deterioration over wide areas may be seen on satellite images in the same way, using the near infrared bands of the multispectral scanner. Obviously it is desirable to spot problems at an early stage while it is still possible to prevent their spread. Remote sensing methods have proved successful in the detection of balsam woolly aphid on fir trees, of spruce budworm, eastern hemlock looper and other insect infestations. In cases where damage has already been extensive, it is possible to assess the resultant loss of wood. For example, a survey of spruce budworm was successfully carried out a few years ago in Fundy National Park. A combination of photo-interpretation of colour-infrared aerial photographs and field work provided information on the extent of the damage, the intensity of defoliation, locations of severe tree mortality and volume loss. Similar experiments with satellite imagery are in progress.

Another form of damage is that due to windstorms.

Sometimes this remains unnoticed in remote areas for a considerable time until the fallen trees, rotting and drying out, become a fire hazard and begin to burn. Examination of satellite pictures allows this to be recognized early so that salvage operations may be carried out. Areas of extensive damage in the Sudbury region in August, 1970, were easily seen on Landsat images soon after the satellite was launched. By this time the trees were dead and easily distinguished from those with live foliage around them; even recent damage is detectable by the use of change detection techniques.

Air pollution is known to be an important cause of damage to trees; sulphur dioxide fumes are the chief culprit. Fumes from industry and mining operations lead to a considerable amount of destruction, which can be readily detected by aerial photography. In the case of a train accident occurring some years ago in Vinsulla, B.C., the sulphur dioxide fumes from the burning wreckage drifted down the North Thompson River Valley a distance of many miles. Aerial photographs recorded the damage to trees as far away as 18 miles. Experiments carried out at Wawa, Ontario, where there are large areas of sulphur dioxide damage, showed that satellite imagery using band 5 of the Landsat multispectral scanner, is also useful in this respect. Comparative tests between observation and sketching from a plane, airborne photography and subsequent interpretation, and satellite imagery showed that despite the much smaller scale given by Landsat, the detection of damage was almost as good and considerably quicker. While airborne sketching took about a week, and photointerpretation about 2 1/2 days, the calculations from satellite photographs took only about half a day - a considerable saving in time and effort. With the use of computer tapes instead of visual imagery, it should be possible to improve on the delineation of boundaries.

A study of wildlife hahitats has occupied the attention of biologists and environmentalists for many years. One of the problems is that most of these areas are remote, and directly man has access to them, something is inevitably changed. Even the noise of low-flying aircraft has a disturbing effect on some of the birds and animals. The only way of surveying such regions is by remote sensing, and satellite imagery has obvious advantages wherever the smaller scale and lower resolution allow it to be used.

In Chapter VII we saw how images from Landsat helped B.C. Hydro in their planning of a new transmission line route; they wished to avoid any installation which might have a deleterious effect on the environment or might destroy the habitats of mountain goats or sheep.

The larger scale of air photography is able to tell us something about form-vegetation features which may serve as a guide to wildlife habitats. A study to investigate this possibility was carried out by the Manitoba Department of Mines, Resources and Environment Management a few years ago in connection with the nesting of Canada geese in the Little Seal River area. The use of colour-infrared film permitted the detection of land-form vegetation units suitable for nesting. At present we do not know enough about the density of nesting of Canada geese in northern areas. Reliable counts are badly needed in order to determine goose production on an annual basis. To carry out such work on the ground in the largely inaccessible regions of northern Manitoba would be an impossible task, but with the help of air photography a comprehensive survey becomes practicable.

The use of a combination of data from aircraft and from satellite has enabled scientists from the Canadian Forestry Service, the Canadian Wildlife Service and the Lands Directorate to carry out a cooperative project on snow goose colonies in the Hudson Bay area. One such colony situated in the Cape Henrietta Marie area is the world's most southerly colony and it is rapidly expanding in population. It became of interest to know more about the rate of expansion and for this a reliable population census technique was required and also a means of classifying terrain, water bodies, and vegetation. For population estimates the researchers chose black and white aerial photographs at a scale of 1:2,000. For getting a good overall view of habitats and their relation to other features they found that Landsat imagery served their purpose, while for the classification of land types colour photographs at a scale 1:10,000 were preferred. Identification of vegetation was effected by using 70 mm photography with colour and colour-infrared film. This is therefore a good example of the use of several types of remote sensing techniques being applied to a problem to good advantage. The whole situation can then be monitored annually.

Remote sensing has also been used to good advantage by the Quebec Wildlife Service in studying some aspects of the beluga whales, snow geese, and larger animals. Visual air surveys have traditionally been used to make a census, where the observer in a plane actually counts the numbers of birds as he passes over them. Understandably this is not very accurate. There is a limit to the number of bodies an individual can count in any given time; it is difficult to grasp all the features such as sex, age, species, etc. while travelling at high speed, and two experts counting over the same area could well differ in their estimates by at least 50%. Photography offers a permanent record which may be studied later at leisure. Vertical photography in which the camera is looking vertically downward has proved to be the best arrangement for census-taking. It is necessary to fly at heights which will not unduly disturb the wildlife below. This may mean altitudes of 4,000 feet or more. At this height an aerial camera with a 10- or 6-inch lens will produce a satisfactory photograph with good detail, as can be seen in Figure 63. This photograph was taken in October, 1975 as part of a study of the population of Greater Snow geese during the spring and fall migration periods along the St. Lawrence River. From such aerial photographs it is possible to take an accurate census of the geese, to distinguish the young from the adults, to determine ranges of brood size, and to obtain sex and age ratios. An expert can also differentiate other types of birds, such as black ducks, pintails and teal.

A study was made in this way of beluga whales. During the summer beluga congregate in very large numbers in certain bays and estuaries adjacent to major straits and sounds in the eastern Arctic. Hitherto their habits had been largely unknown and the only observations had been visual ones. Vertical air photography using both panchromatic and colour film yielded a great deal more detail on several aspects of the biology of these whales. Counts were obtained on the herds, and the length of a number of whales was measured; this data together with the evaluation of the colour and social relationships between individuals was used

Courtesy of Québec Dept. of Tourism, Game and Fish.

Biological Research Service.

Figure 62. Photograph for Census-Taking of Snow Geese.

to calculate calf production.

Another interesting project involving wildlife concerned the salmon population in B.C. and the environmental changes that might be brought about by construction work on new port facilities in the Fraser River estuary. The port at Robert's Bank at the mouth of the Fraser River was constructed in the late 1960's, but was proving inadequate for the increasing traffic. The authorities wished to expand the facility but feared the effects of further construction on the environment. The estuary is an essential element in the wildlife of the area. It is the migration route for the largest single salmon run in Canada - in fact, one of the largest in the world, and significant losses of fisheries and wildlife habitats would be calamitous to the fishing industry. Large areas of eel grass grow within the boundaries of its waters and this is of great importance both as a habitat for juvenile salmonids and as a spawning ground for herring. Eel grass was therefore the key to the situation as far as the breeding of salmon and herring was concerned, and the question became "Would further construction in the port area reduce the size of the eel grass meadow?". Its extent could be measured by airborne photography, but monitoring it on a regular basis would be extremely expensive. The Canada Centre for Remote Sensing therefore undertook a study to determine whether satellite imagery would be sufficiently accurate for the measurement of intertidal vegetation. Scientists used aerial photography as a base reference and compared the accuracies obtainable by airborne and spaceborne methods. They found that the best way of using Landsat data for the assessment of areal coverage was by means of the unsupervised classification of digital data, while the best way of delineating intertidal vegetation was by means of a colour composite. All four bands of the multispectral scanner were used for the digital analysis and a novel way of enhancing the image was employed to produce the colour composite. Bands 4 and 5 were intensity stretched and illuminated with blue light and green light respectively. A third channel of data resulting from bands (6-5) divided by bands (6+5) was also intensity stretched and illuminated with a red light. This gave the best enhancement and thus the best delineation.

As mentioned before, one of the great advantages of Landsat is that we can go back to past records and pull out of the hat, so to speak, data on topics which were not even envisaged at the time of the original imagery. Satellite products, images and tapes, were in this case able to provide the only records available of the behaviour of the environment from 1973 onwards. This has proved of inestimable value in assessing the damage already done and in monitoring the present and future. Fortunately the records have shown that very little deterioration has been caused by the existing port facility and this bodes well for the future. Expansion has now been started and a careful watch will be kept to check that no permanent changes are brought about in the size of the eel grass meadows. A certain amount will inevitably be removed during dredging operations, but this should be replaced by future growth. The National Harbours Board has expressed itself as being very pleased with these results and as a result the method is now being used operationally.

Mention has already been made in Chapter VI of the Thematic Mapper (TM). Simulated Thematic Mapper data can be produced using an airborne multispectral scanner similar to that carried aboard existing Landsat satellites but with better resolution. The existing situation at Robert's Bank Port has been recorded by Landsat-3 as just described, as well as by simulated TM data. The object of this is to provide a bank of data which will give a reference base for future operation.

These results proved so interesting that the experiment was followed by another, also in the Fraser River Estuary, designed to monitor the distribution of major communities of marshlands using satellite data. C.C.R.S. scientists are working with scientists at the British Columbia Research Council and other local agencies to develop an operational monitoring programme for these important wildlife hahitats, which will use the Thematic Mapper data in Landsat-4. This should ensure that no net loss of marshland occurs in the estuary. Given the large area to be covered, the complexity of the marshland ecosystems and the requirement for repeated observations, satellite remote sensing is the only practical method of undertaking this task.

The examples given in this chapter together with the two previous ones have shown, without a doubt, how valuable remote-sensing methods can be. By combining several forms of airborne and spaceborne imagery we can make the best use of each. Aerial photography is a well-established procedure, but it is by no means static; new techniques are being developed all the time. Space imagery is a relatively recent procedure, but the progress made in applying it to so many areas and problems is nothing short of phenomenal. It will be interesting to see what the future will reveal as new sensors with higher resolution, both spatial and spectral, come into use.

INDEX

---

* Since C.C.R.S. has been involved in the design and testing of so many items of equipment and in the carrying out of so many experiments both by themselves and in conjunction with others, it has been impractical to list them all under this heading. Details will be found in the entries of the particular items themselves.

INDEX

INDEX

INDEX